D1487505

# NAZIH ZUHDI

"Dr. Zuhdi has been working in the field of open heart surgery virtually since its beginning. His major contributions were made quite a long time ago, and therefore today seem almost conventional wisdom ..."

John W. Kirklin, M.D.
Professor of Surgery
Division of Cardiothoracic Surgery
University of Alabama, 1991

Mitsuno Ready PSA

# NAZIH ZUHDI

*private papers and personal portraits*

VOLUME I / 1950-1965

FROM TIMELESS SANDS TO RED CLAY | VISION BEYOND THE NEXT HORIZON

## THROUGH THE EYES OF A MAN WHO LIVED IT

**Brooks Barr, Ph.D.**

Copyright 2014 By Nazih Zuhdi

All the correspondence and documents of Dr. Nazih Zuhdi
published in this book are preserved at
the Research Division of the Oklahoma Historical Society,
a National Archives Affiliate, located at
the Oklahoma History Center,
800 Nazih Zuhdi Drive, Oklahoma City, Oklahoma 73105-7917


Special gratitude to the following persons and entities for their gracious
permission in the use of their works both literary and artistic:
David Cooper
Oklahoma Heritage Association
Oklahoma History Center

ISBN - 978-1-938923-10-4
Library of Congress Control No. 2014942233

Editor: Gini Moore Campbell
Associate Editor: Annette McMichael Zuhdi
Editorial Assistance: Rose Lane

Published by the Oklahoma Heritage Association
Book Cover and Layout by Nathan Dunn
1400 Classen Drive
Oklahoma City, OK 73106

Printed in Canada

# NAZIH ZUHDI

## From Timeless Sands to Red Clay
## Vision Beyond The Next Horizon
## Through the Eyes of a Man Who Lived It

An aura of dignity and integrity
surrounds Dr. Thomas N. Lynn.

So many owe him so much.

## Dedicated To Dr. Thomas N. Lynn

**Dean**
>University of Oklahoma
>College of Medicine (1974-1979)

**Vice-President of Medical and Scientific Affairs**
>Baptist Hospital, Oklahoma City (1980-1995)

**Co-Founder**
**Member, Board of Directors**
>Thomas N. Lynn Institute for Health Care Research

M. Rose Elizabeth Power, RSM, stands atop the mountain, gazes in wonder at the world around her and exclaims:

"Our life's journey Epiphany and Genius occassionally cross paths. When Dr. Nazih Zuhdi's Genius met Mercy's holy ground, an Epiphany illuminated a path which in time transcended the Globe. This blessed gift birthed a channel of hope, of joy, and continuance of life for multitudes."

*The Life of Nazih Zuhdi: Uncharted Voyage of a Heart*, by Brooks Barr, Ph.D., is included in the Heritage Room at the convent at Mercy Hospital, Oklahoma City, Oklahoma. The Heritage Room is a collection of Mercy Hospital's history and statements dating back to the 1831 Catherine McAuley—with its history in Oklahoma dating back to 1884.

-M. Rose Elizabeth Power, RSM
Sister of Mercy

# INTRODUCTION

The book you hold in your hands is a road map—an invitation to explore the landscape of human achievement. The land on which we stand and thrive is not merely the product of natural forces, but of the toil of many men and women who shaped the world that is ours today. A few of these pioneers have built mountains—singular works that tower over the geography like eternal beacons. A fewer still have climbed such heights and continued a lifetime's labor, raising a range of peaks that redefine the terrain of our lives.

Nazih Zuhdi and the worlds of his mentors have left a trail of such crests—places where one can stand and marvel at how the mind of man can create a new and better world. I invite you to climb some of those crests with me, to wonder and delight at what you see through the stories that are told.

The scope of Nazih Zuhdi's work spans wide—one gaze cannot encompass it. This will be the first of three volumes—the first will focus on his early days with Clarence Dennis and C. Walton Lillehei (July 1, 1952-December, 1956) and then move on to his independent work in his laboratories at the University of Oklahoma College of Medicine in Oklahoma City (1957-1958) and at 13th Street Mercy Hospital in Oklahoma City (1958-1965); the second will fix our eyes on the years he spent at Integris Baptist Medical Center, (1959, 1963-1999); and finally we will look specifically at the years since 2000.

So climb these peaks with me, as well as so many others. From our vantage points we will see the panorama of human innovation as it reshapes the landscape of modern medicine. From these "mountaintops" one can see fresh worlds of science, wonder and beauty that stretch far beyond the next horizon.

Yousef Khanfar

*T*o she who holds in her person every measure of grace that God may bestow, and has had the charity to shower it on my life. Her heart is the fountain from which I draw my strength, and the spring that flows out and bathes her family and all who know her. She is beauty beyond the most elegant rose, and radiance beyond the most incandescent star. She is quite simply, my love and my life — my dearest Annette — my "Annie."

— Your Nazih

*The words of the poem fly from my heart to hers, my beloved Annie. I gratefully acknowledge that Brooks Barr gave them the Shakespearean grandeur. From his vast collection, Yousef Khanfar chose the landscape with a ray of life in it.*

# FOR SISTER MARY COLETTA

1958-1965
Transformed Community Straw
Into Research Gold

She was my friend, my Godsent collaborator.
When Baptist was but a pasture, a field of dreams,
She extended the hand of welcome and support,
Our aims were one.
With her, our aspirations became brick and mortar
Stocked with the finest tools run by the brightest minds.
She sheltered our group from prejudice with her wise counsel.
Barriers of ignorance crumbled before her paramount force,
All that for which the world has heaped its honors and love.
My workings of hemodilution and the artificial bypass heart,
All that was achieved with her at Mercy.

But alas! Every golden age has its tarnished end.
The luster of precious metal lost in the fire of human folly,
The pride of pioneers filled all those who were the early band of hearts.
Our work, rare and revered; our egos fed by adulation,
The day came when she didn't call; at the drop of a slight I walked.
The call never came, and thus began my life at Baptist.

But just as youth has its brashness, age brings its wisdom.
With the folly of the young we believed ourselves an inestimable diamond.
Had I humbled myself and picked up the phone myself,
A rift would be breached, and Baptist would be Mercy again.
Now I can look back across the years and sweep away the arrogance,
Humility schools the haughty and now I can say
"Dear sister, the fault was mine."

*Brooks Barr expressed my thoughts into poetic English.*

# MERCY HEALTH CENTER

4300 West Memorial Road
Oklahoma City, Okla. 73120 (405) 755-1515

CONDUCTED BY SISTERS OF MERCY

To Dr. Nazih Zuhdi,

Through his special genetic gifts. Dr. Nazih Zuhdi inspired brilliant clarity of vision which influenced the depths of cardiovascular surgery, cardiovascular medicine, and beyond. His genius introduced healing and life for many throughout the world.

M. Rose Elizabeth Power, RSM
Sister of Mercy
September 24, 2011

COMMITMENT TO EXCELLENCE

## DR. NAZIH ZUHDI

Your tale is a true inspiration, and it is beautiful how you are chronicling your story. To be an innovator in an industry is amazing, but to be part of one that literally breathes life into someone is beyond most people's imagination.

*Kimberly Siess*

## A NOD TO THOSE WHO HAVE GONE BEFORE ME

As my eyes travel back along the steps of my life charted in this book, I am humbled by the sight of the massive mountains on which I have set my footprint. The immensity of my work I will leave to the judgment of history. What I do know is that it would not have been possible without the work of two men who came before me and for a blessed time allowed me to walk alongside them—Drs. Clarence Dennis and C. Walton Lillehei. Whenever my name is mentioned, their names should be remembered, and it is with gratitude and affection that I recognize and honor their monumental achievements.

# THE ELEVATION OF THE COMMUNITY HOSPITAL REACHING FROM THE PRAIRIE TO OLYMPUS

When Nazih Zuhdi moved to Mercy Hospital and set up his experimental laboratory there, his work marked more than a revolution in the reputation of Oklahoma medical science. Perhaps even more influentially, in the years that followed, first at Mercy Hospital and later at Baptist Hospital, Zuhdi was remaking the image of what was possible in a community hospital and elevating its mission in the world.

The new possibilities in open heart surgery willed into existence in community hospitals everywhere a constellation of accompanying laboratories—cardiac catheterization being one among many such corollaries and ancillaries—and other disciplines, along with the expertise to exercise them.

Because of what Zuhdi accomplished in Oklahoma, community hospitals all over the world were awaking to the idea that they too could reach for the stars. Zuhdi had expanded the very definition of the community hospital.

*Brooke Barry*

"I think my interpretation is that the University in addition to this rift that occurred [between Zuhdi and the medical school] viewed Baptist as the biggest challenge to the University on medical expertise, and here was this community hospital doing things that the University hospital ought to be doing.

In other words, Baptist Hospital because of Zuhdi, and galvanized by Nazih Zuhdi, Allen Greer and John Carey, became a distinctive hospital besides general hospitals. And, as I understand it, the same might be said regarding Mercy Hospital."

*Tom Lynn*

**Dr. Thomas Lynn**
**Dean, University of Oklahoma**
**College of Medicine (1974-1979)**

# THE HUMAN HEART IN ONE LIFE

The story of the human heart in modern medicine can readily be limned in the life of a man—a man who forged his dreams at the throbbing edge of innovation. That man is Dr. Nazih Zuhdi. Dr. John Kirklin, one of the original pioneers in the field of open heart surgery, strongly supported the nomination of Dr. Nazih Zuhdi for the American College of Cardiology's Distinguished Scientist Award. Kirklin wrote in his letter of August 14, 1991:

"Dr Zuhdi has been working in the field of open-heart surgery virtually since its beginning ..."

Nazih Zuhdi's tale begins in Dr. Clarence Dennis' laboratories and surgical services at the State University of New York—Downstate Medical Center for the period July 1, 1952-June 30, 1956. From that fountain can be traced the momentous story of man's mastery of this remarkable organ. Again, in his letter of August 12, 1991, Dennis strongly supported the nomination of Dr. Nazih Zuhdi for the American College of Cardiology's Distinguished Scientist Award:

"During his training at Brooklyn, Zuhdi was a very bright star among the 50-odd residents in training there, always ready with suggestions and the drive to carry them through, which he did regularly in the year he worked with me in the research laboratory during our work on developing a pump-oxygenator, *as a result of which* we were able to salvage the first long term survivor of massive myocardial infarction and shock by temporary circulatory support with that same pump-oxygenator."

That was performed on November 1, 1954—and seven months later, on June 30, 1955, Dennis performed the sixth successful open-heart surgery with cardio-pulmonary bypass in the nation. The operation was a complete success, and the patient was dismissed to a healthy life. This was the first case of open heart surgery using a heart-lung machine in the state of New York, and the second in the eastern part of the country.

Dennis compiled, as of that date, June 30, 1955, all the successful open-heart operations using the pump-oxygenator. In addition to his one success out of three attempts, he found, "John Gibbon had one success on May 6, 1953 in five attempts, John Kirklin by 1955 was reported to have done eight open-heart cases with a modification of Gibbon's device, with four survivors"—his first successful one was on March 22, 1955. However, C. Walton Lillehei did use the bubble oxygenator of DeWall-Lillehei on May 13, 1955 and it was not successful. On July 12, 1955 (barely beyond June 30, 1955) Lillehei used it successfully.

From that self-same start, the heart-lung machine can be seen to bifurcate in two directions—dually first to the repair of heart defects, and second to the development of artificial devices to assist or replace the defective heart. Both trends were accelerated into fruition by Zuhdi's independent research work and its clinical surgical applications of Total Intentional Hemodilution at the 13th Street Mercy Hospital Heart and Research Institute in Oklahoma City, Oklahoma.

Nazih Zuhdi continued his education and training with C. Walton Lillehei at the University of Minnesota starting in July of 1956. Lillehei had already gained the title, "King of Hearts," partially because of his unique extensive experience repairing heart defects using "cross-circulation," a compatible human as the heart-lung machine.

Nazih Zuhdi studied a catalogue of cardiac defects and specific research of the DeWall-Lillehei pump-oxygenator and its sheet derivative in the cardiovascular division of Lillehei. Nazih Zuhdi was designated a "Co-Worker" by Clarence Dennis and a "Master Surgeon" by C. Walton Lillehei. They both assured him that going to Oklahoma would be the field for him to be "The King of the Prairies"—Nazih Zuhdi went beyond that. C. Walton Lillehei reminded Nazih Zuhdi after a long day of work "remember, you can do it all."

In October of 1957, Nazih Zuhdi moved to Oklahoma—a land where open-heart surgery, heart-lung machines, artificial hearts, and corresponding experimental research and clinical applications were virtually non-existing. In the early fifties, American Board Certification did not even conceive of open heart surgery and heart-lung machines. Settling in Oklahoma, Zuhdi WAS open-heart surgery and its derivatives there ... from which he paved its course around the world.

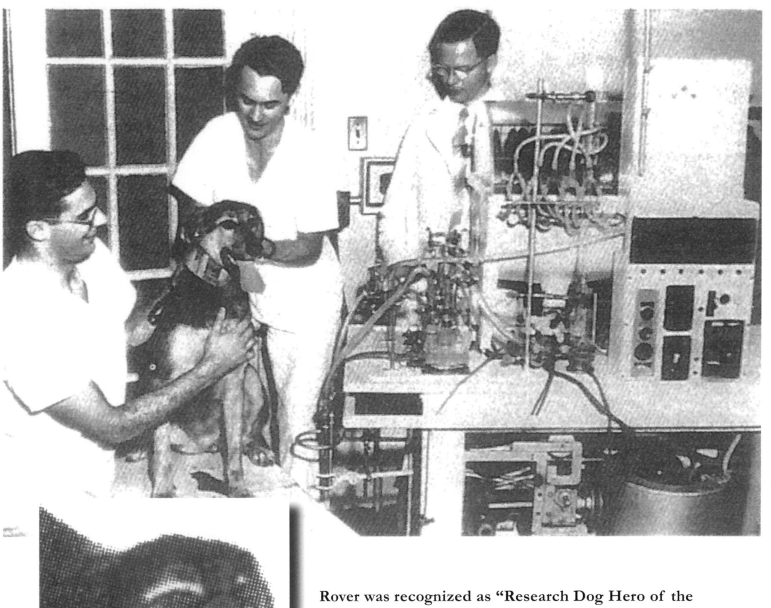

Rover was recognized as "Research Dog Hero of the Year, 1952." A collar and a plaque were awarded by the New York State Society of Medical Research . From left to right are Nazih Zuhdi's co-collaborators Charles C. Fries, Constantine Pereyma, and pioneering Chief Clarence Dennis. The successful perfusion of a dog in the laboratory inspired other researchers to proceed full speed in the realization of such an endeavor. Rover became the canine embodiment of the possibilities that lay ahead. *Printed with permission of Transactions of the American Society of Artificial Internal Organs, 1989.*

This is the story of how cardiopulmonary discipline developed in this country—introducing the players and how Nazih Zuhdi interacted with them and how he ultimately put this experience together and came to the synthesis of all the efforts of the pioneers, conceiving and producing his final solution of Total Intentional Hemodilution that captured the world.

Dr. Thomas N. Lynn
Dean, University of Oklahoma
College of Medicine (1974-1979)
Oklahoma City, Ok.

**PHOTOGRAPH BY JIM MEEKS, CURATOR OF EXHIBITS, OKLAHOMA HISTORY CENTER, 800 NAZIH ZUHDI DRIVE, OKLAHOMA CITY, OK**: *Nazih Zuhdi's double helical reservoir heart-lung machine, a modification of the DeWall-Lillehei Heart-Lung Machine, which brought about his final solution to total body perfusion, open-heart surgery and bloodless surgery into reality—1957-1960. In the background is the Zuhdi-Ritchie Artificial Bypass Heart of 1964.*

*The following letter was scanned in its entirety.*

**Denton A. Cooley, M. D.**
Texas Heart Institute
In The Texas Medical Center
Houston, Texas 77030

August 18, 1999

Nazih Zuhdi, M.D.
Oklahoma Transplantation Institute
Integris Baptist Medical Center
3300 Northwest Expressway
Oklahoma City, OK 73112

Dear Nazih:

As you approach retirement from clinical practice I join your many admirers, grateful students and patients, and friends in wishing you good health and happiness.

Your career in surgery has truly been outstanding with many "firsts" in cardiovascular surgery. Of all those I believe your early investigations of blood substitutes in cardiopulmonary bypass was the most useful and practical. Your courage to apply this principle in clinical surgery made open heart surgery safer and available to large numbers of patients. Although skeptics of this departure from standard practice were vocal and often emotional, you persisted and convinced the entire surgical profession of the validity of this technique.

Throughout your impressive career you have followed a fearless path to further progress. The development of organ transplantation at your Institute is testimony to your eagerness to achieve.

From my earliest acquaintance with you in the era of exploration of the cardiac chambers, I have enjoyed your inspiring approach to innovations. Also, I have enjoyed your friendship and hospitable spirit.

Good luck in the years ahead.

Sincerely yours,

Denton A. Cooley, M.D.

DAC:jm

"Dr. Zuhdi, in the late 1950s, was the originator, creator, and inventor of hemodilution and the non-blood prime of the pump oxgenator for open heart surgery ... It's ironic that the history of the technique that is so effective and so universally used has been largely lost upon the recent generation of surgeons and cardiologists, not to mention our patients."

*Dr. C. Walton Lillehei*
*Professor of Surgery Emeritus*
*University of Minnesota, 1995*

"... Such as Nazih Zuhdi ... who worked with us during this training and who later conceived and introduced the technique of hemodilution in open-heart work ..."

*Dr. Clarence Dennis*
*1985 Laureate Address*
*American Society of Artificial Internal Organs*

"Dr. Zuhdi has been working in the field of open-heart surgery virtually since its beginning. His major contributions were made quite a long time ago, and therefore today seem almost conventional wisdom. However, it is Dr. Zuhdi who introduced the use of hemodilution ..."

*John W. Kirklin, M.D.*
*Professor of Surgery*
*Division of Cardiothoracic Surgery*
*University of Alabama, 1991*

Dr. Allen Greer   1918-1999

Dr. Allen Greer from October 1957 until he passed away in the year 1999 was a protector of Dr. Nazih Zuhdi. Dr. Zuhdi states unequivocally that Dr. Greer was primary in his staying in Oklahoma. In Greer's induction in 1992 into the Oklahoma Hall of Fame of the Oklahoma Heritage Association, it was officially stated: "Greer has been instrumental in the development of modern cardiac surgery in Oklahoma. He recognized Nazih Zuhdi's abilities and provided the environment for him to do his research and original developments, and he assisted him in the following advancements: development of a technologically advanced heart-lung machine, which made open heart surgery on a mass scale practical for the first time, experimental artificial heart work; the first coronary artery bypass surgery in Oklahoma, and the first heart transplant, the first heart-lung transplant, and the first unilateral lung transplant in Oklahoma." The statement continues highlighting his numerous civic accomplishments. Dr. Zuhdi was inducted into the Oklahoma Hall of Fame of the Oklahoma Heritage Association in 1994, so they became brothers in that remarkable and inspirational fraternity.

Richard Green, profiling Allen Greer for the *Oklahoma State Journal of Medicine* in March of 1996, stated that Greer "does credit Zuhdi with the idea and the research for perhaps the group's single, most important innovation, hemodilution."

When I visit my mother's grave in Rose Hill Cemetery, I also visit his — He is close by.

# ETCHED IN PERPETUITY

Nazih Zuhdi, M.D. is the only Oklahoman included in ALL four epochal affirmations for his Oklahoma-based research, leading to and including his Total Intentional Hemodilution.

**"Milestones of Cardiovascular Medicine" 1628-1989**
**The American College of Cardiology**
**The 361 years of pioneers**
**In the Evolution of Cardiovascular Medicine**
**Nazih Zuhdi, M.D.(1963-1964)**

**"Heart Surgery Founders Group"**
**Dwight Harken, M.D., Cambridge, Massachusetts**
**Nazih Zuhdi, M.D.(1953, 1955, 1956, 1970, 1960)**

**"Pioneers in Cardiac Surgery"**
**Stephen Westaby, M.D., Oxford, England**
**Cecil Bosher, Toronto, Canada**
**Nazih Zuhdi, M.D.(1953, 1955, 1956, 1970, 1960)**

**"World Who's Who in Science:**
**A Biographical Dictionary of Notable**
**Scientists from Antiquity to the Present"**
**Allen G. Debus, University of Chicago, Chicago, Illinois**
**Nazih Zuhdi, M.D. (1968)**

# AMERICAN COLLEGE OF CARDIOLOGY
## "MILESTONES OF CARDIOVASCULAR MEDICINE" 1628-1989
## "DEDICATED TO ALL THOSE WHO HAVE CONTRIBUTED IN THE FIELD OF CARDIOVASCULAR MEDICINE"

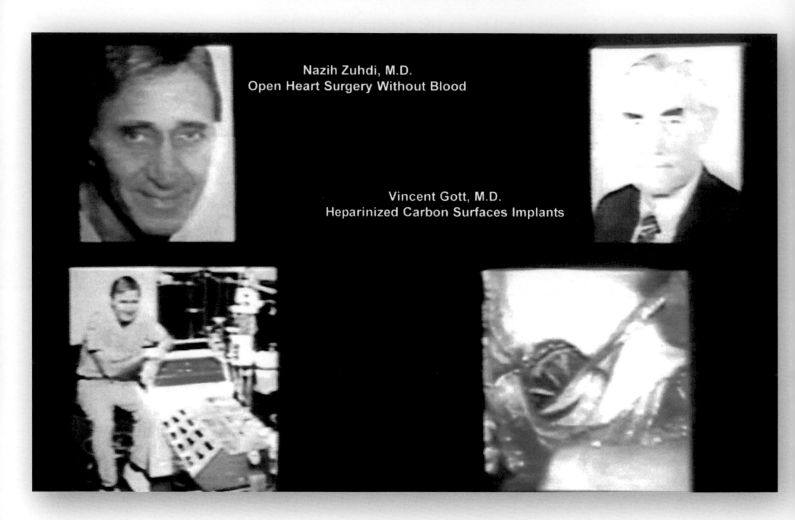

A Frame from the "Milestones of Cardiovascular Medicine." Dr. Nazih Zuhdi and Dr. Vincent Gott were co-trainees in the cardiovascular service of Dr. C. Walton Lillehei at the University of Minnesota, Minneapolis, Minnesota (1956). Dr. Gott retired as Professor Emeritus, Johns Hopkins University Cardiac Surgery.

The Heart House in Washington, D. C., the American College of Cardiology, a most prestigious association dedicated to medicine of the heart, honors the giants whose steps have brought us to the threshold of our contemporary, wondrous capabilities. "Milestones of Cardiovascular Medicine" is a documentary that traces an odyssey that spans the centuries. It begins in 1628, when William Harvey first established the principle of the circulation of the blood, and journeys through the years to the modern era of cardiovascular medicine into the entire field of medicine. Before our eyes parade the faces and names and contributions of each of the titans that have spurred the quest for what was once the unthinkable.

Yes, the only work originated and experimentally completed on Oklahoma's red clay to be recognized as one of the "Milestones of Cardiovascular Medicine" is the work of Nazih Zuhdi—"Total Intentional Hemodilution" opened the gates to all that followed in that discipline—including surgery without blood. He walked the path with those who came before him; he cleared the road for those who came after him. The first clinical application was performed on February 25, 1960 by Nazih Zuhdi, Allen Greer, John Carey, John Montroy, Wiley McCollum, Modine Pierce, Betty Blackburn, Mary Spencer, Peggy Johnson, Ida Bearhead, Florene Wallace and Sister Mary Alvera—at 13th Street Mercy Hospital, Oklahoma City. All paths then led to Oklahoma City.

The 13th Street Mercy Hospital Heart and Research Institute—Experimental Laboratory, the University of Oklahoma Health Sciences Center and the Oklahoma Medical Research Foundation provided laboratories that, with their distinct strengths and attributes, have been welcome venues for the experimental work of Zuhdi and his team over the past forty years.

# HALF A CENTURY LATER ...

### A word on life takes on
### a life of its own

On September 9, 2011, "The Latest CNN News" chose to do a feature on "Cardiac Surgery: A Blessing of Medical Science for Cardiac Patients." Of four paragraphs dedicated to tracing the history of Open Heart Surgery, the article devoted an entire, distinctive paragraph to the ground-breaking work of Dr. Nazih Zuhdi, the only pioneer singled out for such attention. Millions have benefited from his medical revolution, but fewer know the name to which they owe the quantity and quality of their lives. Now, through CNN News, that name will live on to a wider audience. A universal authority has granted the name of Nazih Zuhdi everlasting life on the Web.

**Society**

Renaissance Ball brings out fun and fashion from locals. Page B-1

**Editorial**

Forget worrying about the Big 12 Conference. Check out our proposal for a new Big Eight.

Page 8

**Sports**

Putnam City North goes two overtimes to pull out slim win.

Page 5

## Opinions from just ONE MAN by J. LELAND GOURLEY

*lgourley@okcfriday.com*

*An editorial is not an order from on high. It is just one man's opinion. JLG, 1974*

### Let's stop that Ponzi talk, Rick

**I** WISH my man, Rick Perry, would quit saying Social Security is a "Ponzi Scheme."

To the millions of voters on Social Security, that sounds like he wants to wipe out the monthly pay check from Uncle Sam. (That's a return on our years of paying more Social Security taxes than is paid back to recipients.)

Get this straight: Rick Perry does not plan on killing your monthly check from Social Security!

[Continued on Page 8]

---

## Oklahoma's Beautiful People by VICKI CLARK

*vcgfriday@aol.com*

### Fall brings our city back to life

**H**URRAY FOR COOL BREEZES, rain, the state fair, everybody being back in town for Renaissance Ball and Marvin Hamlisch at the Armstrong Auditorium and CityRep starting its fall season with the *Last Night of Ballyhoo*, this week. It gets lonely around here in the summer. **Gene Rainbolt** and granddaughters rode the Siberian Express and half of Fridayland flocked to La Jolla for **Sandy Meyers** birthday. (See both stories in our *Saturday Society* mag on the 29th)

The ball was great.

[Continued on Page B-1]

---

**Excursions by JOY**

---

# okc*FRIDAY*

*The Newspaper for Oklahoma's Trendsetters*

Vol. 45 No. 20 • Two Sections 18 Pages

**September 16, 2011**

**okcfriday.com** f facebo

*Serving affluent far north Oklahoma City, Nichols Hil...*

**SEA LIONS AT THE** Oklahoma State Fair perform their annual routine. This ... which began Thursday and lasts until Sept. 25, will be the last for the sea li...

## BOUND FOR NEW SEA

*2011 last chance to catch State Fair's sea lion...*

**By RYAN PIERSOL**
*OKC Friday*

There's plenty new to see at this year's Oklahoma State Fair, but the must-see might be one of the fair's long-time favorites.

That's because this fair, which began Thursday, will be the final opportunity to catch a performance at the Sea Lion Splash. After five years of entertaining Oklahomans, the sea lions and their trainers are moving on.

"They've been very popular. They're one of our most popular attractions," said Scott Munz, Vice President of Marketing and Public Relations with the fair. "It's just that we don't typically run things at the fair past the five-year mark and

this is their fifth y... fair."

The sea lions r... 9,300-gallon pool... Bandshell Lawn.... form three times... can usually be se... in their pool thro... day. The fair has... ly made it possib... tors to have their...

[Continued...

---

## Village close to earning funds for splash pad

**By RYAN PIERSOL**
*OKC Friday*

The city of the Village is getting close to reaching a long-held goal to build a splash pad, but could still use some help for its upcoming Fun Fair.

The Sixth Annual Fun Fair will be Oct. 15 at Duffner Park. Each of the previous

ing water.

City Treasurer Beverly Whitener said that the city is hopeful that, after this year's fair, they'll have enough money to at least build the splash pad portion of a project that is expected to cost $200,000. The splash pad, without all the accompanying ameni-

## Hap...

---

# Dr. Zuhdi featured on CNN

World renowned heart surgeon and Fridaylander Dr. Nazih Zuhdi was featured on the Latest CNN News as part of its "Cardiac Surgery: A blessing of medical science for Cardiac patients" segment.

The article, posted under the Health tab at

**NAZIH ZUHDI**

www.latestcnnnews.com, credits Zuhdi with performing open heart surgery using Total Intentional Hemodilution, the technique he invented, on Terry Gene Nix, age 7, on Feb. 25, 1960, at Mercy Hospital in Oklahoma City. It also describes the first open heart surgery performed on a child, in March, 1961, using Total Intentional Hemodilution, by Zuhdi, Dr. John Carey and Dr. Allen Greer.

In addition, CNN reported that Zuhdi performed the first heart transplant in Oklahoma on Nancy Rogers at Baptist Hospital. **SUCCESSFUL.***

*The placement of Successful in this position is for clarity.*

*The following report is reprinted exactly as it was presented
on the Internet by Latest CNN News, September 9, 2011*

## Half a century later ...

# Cardiac Surgery: A blessing of medical science for Cardiac patients

**Latest CNN News: Beating heart is a sign of life. With the passage of time the heart diseases are getting serious and serious and the human efforts to cure them are also increasing. A major advancement in this regard is cardiac surgery. Its different types are being described and explained below.**

**Open Heart Surgery:**

**Open heart surgery is a surgery in which the patient's heart is opened and surgery is performed on the internal structures of the heart. It was soon discovered by Dr. Wilfred G. Bigelow of the UniversityofToronto that the repair of intracardiac pathologies was better done with a bloodless and motionless environment, which means that the heart should be stopped and drained of blood. The first successful intracardiac correction of a congenital heart defect using hypothermia was performed by Dr. C. Walton Lillehei and Dr. F. John Lewis at the UniversityofMinnesota on September 2, 1952. The following year, Soviet surgeon Aleksandr Aleksandrovich Vishnevskiy conducted the first cardiac surgery under local anesthesia.**

Cardiac Surgery: A blessing of medical science for Cardiac patients | Latest CNN News  Page 2 of 7
**September 9, 2011**

Surgeons realized the limitations of hypothermia – complex intracardiac repairs take more time and the patient needs blood flow to the body, particularly to the brain. The patient needs the function of the heart and lungs provided by an artificial method, hence the termcardiopulmonary bypass. Dr. John Heysham Gibbon at Jefferson Medical School in Philadelphia reported in 1953 the first successful use of extracorporeal circulation by means of an oxygenator, but he abandoned the method, disappointed by subsequent failures. In 1954 Dr. Lillehei realized a successful series of operations with the controlled cross-circulation technique in which the patient's mother or father was used as a 'heart-lung machine'. Dr. John W. Kirklin at the Mayo Clinic in Rochester, Minnesotastarted using a Gibbon type pump-oxygenator in a series of successful operations, and was soon followed by surgeons in various parts of the world.

Nazih Zuhdi performed the first total intentional hemodilution open heart surgery on Terry Gene Nix, age 7, on February 25, 1960, at Mercy Hospital, Oklahoma City, OK. The operation was a success; however, Nix died three years later in 1963. In March, 1961, Zuhdi, Carey, and Greer, performed open heart surgery on a child, age 3½, using the total intentional hemodilution machine. In 1985 Dr. Zuhdi performedOklahoma's first successful heart transplant on Nancy Rogers at Baptist Hospital. The transplant was successful, butRogers, a cancer sufferer, died from an infection 54 days after surgery.

# A WORD FROM OUR STATE'S HISTORIAN

Throughout Dr. Zuhdi's remarkable life, he has earned many titles. He is a scientist, a healer, a humanitarian, an innovator, and a mentor. He is a philosopher, a dreamer, a team-builder, and a man of peace. Fortunately for all of us, he is also an Oklahoman.

He came to our young state with skills and ambition, armed with lessons learned from a family whose roots grow deep in the soils of ancient cultures. Here, he found opportunity to build something new and met kindred spirits willing to help overcome challenges and push back the frontiers of science.

He never gave up, never let the voices of doubt deter him from his dreams to save lives and help people. His accomplishments in the laboratory have changed the course of medical history around the world. His services to patients have changed the lives of fathers, mothers, sons, and daughters. He will long be remembered as a generous soul who believed that we should live in peace and harmony. His legacy is assured.

Bob L. Blackburn, Ph.D.
Oklahoma Historical Society

Nazih Zuhdi, M.D.

My own humble contribution to the story of Nazih Zuhdi and his work is born of hundreds and thousands of hours spent with the man himself and his papers—what he has written and what others have written about him. Every sentence and every word has been submitted to Zuhdi himself for correction and confirmation and tweaked to his ruthless sense of truthfulness. Every word has his approval, and the veracity of the work rests on the rock of his implacable integrity.

**Brooks Barr, Ph.D.**
**Adjunct Professor**
**Theatre History, Religion and the Arts**
**Saint Edwards University**
**Austin, Texas**

**Archivist and Biographer of Nazih Zuhdi**
**Author of** *The Life of Nazih Zuhdi:*
*Uncharted Voyage of a Heart*
Available at Amazon.com for Kindle, iPhone and iPad

# RIVERS OF THOUGHT, THE ORIGINS OF THIS BOOK

The origins of any new principle or procedure are often lost in the complex of medical science. Dwight A. Harken at the Harvard Medical School warned against anecdotal medical testimony, frequently inaccurate, poorly recalled, and colored by will, emotion, dramatic self motivation.

Lael Wertenbakerr,
*To Mend the Heart*, 1980

Dwight Harken included Zuhdi in his "Heart Surgery Founders Group," the only Oklahoman so honored for his work in 1953, 1955, 1956, 1960 and 1970.

The literary sources of this book consist primarily of three streams. The first is material from my book *The Life of Nazih Zuhdi: Uncharted Voyage of a Heart*. The second river is original essays and letters from notable persons in his life. Especially central to the book is a previously unpublished series of letters that were written in support of the nomination of Nazih Zuhdi for the American College of Cardiology's "Distinguished Scientist Award" in 1991. These letters appear here through the grace of Dr. David Cooper, the former Scientist-in-Residence at the Oklahoma Transplant Center, later renamed the Nazih Zuhdi Transplant Institute.

The final and largest contribution is a remarkable series of "infotorials" published in the weekly newspaper *Friday* from 2008 to early 2011. Dr. Zuhdi chose to initiate these infotorials— mostly half-page editorials consisting of both text and visual appeal—for a very simple reason. By 1991 Professor John Kirklin's authoritative declaration—that Zuhdi's principles of Total Intentional Hemodilution had become the "conventional wisdom"—had been confirmed by other titan pioneers throughout the medical world. The publication of Zuhdi's biography in 2005 was itself a complete, fully cited rendition of his achievements.

Nevertheless, creeping into the public records were errors concerning a very significant body of work that had happened in Oklahoma. To school the community Zuhdi chose the weekly newspaper *Friday*, which circulated among many of the most influential citizens in the state of Oklahoma, as the most appropriate and accessible venue for this mission of education and clarification. What was at stake was quite simply the loss of the creation of a specific medical science in Oklahoma—beyond and totally separate from a competent craftsmanship. It was wrought into something more—the vision to create.

That vision, which begins with and is founded in Zuhdi's principles of Total Intentional Hemodilution—the deliberate priming of the heart-lung machine with a calculated volume of a totally non-blood prime—ushered in one of the milestones in modern medicine. Right in Oklahoma, and for a time Oklahoma City was the focus of world-wide attention. That is a story of which every Oklahoman can be proud—of every person who values dreams sought and attained, especially in the rich tapestry that is the American dream. That is why the story of the dream is in your hands, as seen through the eyes of so many who witnessed it unfold among them.

These are their intimate portraits of the man, in word and picture, especially the ravishing and evocative artistry of Yousef Khanfar in Volume I, Harold "H" Holden in Volume II and Shan Gray in Volume III. Read and look—and wherever your eyes may fall, be stirred.

Yousef Khanfar

"Profound scientific discoveries and changes involve creativity and vision that often may be associated more with art than science. This book elegantly illustrates and combines art and scientific perspective in a way that subtly and creatively suggests those dynamic relationships. The ability to combine art and science, or science and art, is an important aspect of Dr. Zuhdi's vision of the world and of humanity.

The ability to reimagine or see the world with new eyes, to adopt and pursue a different perspective, coupled with the will, talent, and determination to realize innovation and change, are qualities that Dr. Zuhdi has consistently demonstrated and combined in changing the medical world and enriching the lives of millions."

*Daniel J. Provo*
August 19, 2011

Geologists tell us that the chain of islands that we call Hawaii is the product of a single "hot spot" in the earth's crust. As the plates of the earth's crust slowly slide over the mantle, the super-hot molten lava below pokes through the crust and creates Hawaii's famous volcanoes and spectacular landscapes. Then the crust moves on, leaving an island to the ravages of time and erosion. Like a force of nature, Zuhdi's legacy first erupted at 13th Street Mercy Hospital, Oklahoma City (1958-1960). This volume is an overview of the mountain of his legacy there.

But as a world moved on, that brilliance remained white hot when he relocated his creative vision to Integris Baptist Hospital, where he would work for over forty years. Climb the peaks with me—see the panorama!

# ALL PATHS LEAD TO
# OKLAHOMA CITY

## Scientists, Surgeons, Visitors
## From All The World

Open-heart surgery in a private hospital
and in many university teaching hospitals
was unheard of—and Zuhdi's Total
Intentional Hemodilution, in 1960, was the
beginning of the avalanche of open-heart
surgery in every nook and cranny of the
world. What some distinct university centers
considered to be their own
property, Nazih Zuhdi broke the barrier
and delivered to all.

# Dr. John Schilling
## 1917-1999
### Chairman, Department of Surgery
### University of Oklahoma College of Medicine (1956-1974)

In 1957, he first beckoned Dr. Nazih Zuhdi to Oklahoma City. His support for him and his work, though it wavered in the beginning, remained steadfast. Though Zuhdi left the University of Oklahoma, where he built his experimental laboratory in the basement of the old medical school library, his friendship and support continued.

### Chairman, Department of Surgery
### University of Washington (1975-1983)

# To Dr. Nazih Zuhdi

One day — I was in the darkness,
And you lit a candle for me.

Bakr Nour, MD, FACS
Professor and Vice-Chair
Department of Surgery
Associate Dean to Clinical Affairs
Weill Cornell Medical College
Qatar

Dr. Bakr Nour

Yousef Khanfar

Special gratitude to the International Award-Winning photographer and author,
Yousef Khanfar for his portraits and for his
gracious permission in the use of his landscapes from his remarkable books,
*Voices of Light* and *In Search of Peace*.

## Salute To The Heart

I believe our mortal heart is full of endless passion;
Knows that life's journey is only a part and not the whole,
Knows how to love again despite all agonies,
Knows how to endure despite all tribulations,
Knows how to flourish despite all melancholies,
And most of all, that heart knows, even death is nothing,
But a short absence and soon we shall meet again.

*Yousef Khanfar*

Yousef Khanfar

# NAZIH ZUHDI: THE LAST OF THE VINTAGE

The early pioneers who crossed an ocean and a continent to California brought a precious, living gift with their dreams of a new life in America. Grapes grew wild in many places, but they carried with their dreams the living cuttings of the grapes from the Old Country that had produced the wine that had been so much a part of the good life they treasured. They grafted this stock onto the shoots they found in Napa Valley and Sonoma Valley and other places in a new land. They did more than create a new life for themselves. The vintages they brought with them created an industry, a lifestyle to thousands and a cause for community around the tables of the world.

Another group of visionary titans, armed with dedication and vision, grafted new stock onto the legacy that is modern medicine. The names were not Chardonnay or Cabernet, but for this crucial formative period for Nazih Zuhdi's path between 1952 and 1956 were Clarence Dennis, John Gibbon, C. Walton Lillehei, John Kirklin and finally, Zuhdi himself (1954, 1957-1960, 1957-1965), who created more than an industry. They created a discipline that has given life to millions, and everything that is open heart surgery has flowed from them as surely as every bottle of wine that comes from the Napa Valley owes its heritage to those original vintages that were their early treasures. Along with the others, Nazih Zuhdi is the name through which and by which open heart surgery and its derivatives were created or attempted beyond a boutique endeavor of a few university centers into an open and safe gift to spread to the world. He was there at its early planting and he himself has grafted his own vision onto the vines. His Total Intentional Hemodilution is the breakthrough that put the wine of safe, dependable open heart surgery on every table. One by one, Dr. Dennis and his "co-workers," for the period July 1951-June 30, 1955, have passed on, all save one. His name is Dr. Nazih Zuhdi, and per an email received by Annette, "Nazih, you are the last of the vintage."

"The vintage." Nazih Zuhdi didn't read about the genesis of open heart surgery and derivatives. He lived it, and it lived through him. His principles of Total Intentional Hemodilution—the deliberate dilution of the blood during open heart surgery and derivatives with a calculated volume of totally non-blood prime of the heart-lung machine—made possible and safe all that followed in that field and found applications in other disciplines of medicine as well. That is why he is so intimately involved in writing all this: to confirm the achievements of the group of pioneers to which he belongs. We all owe our hearts to them, and it is to them that we raise our glasses in an eternal toast.

"God wills it"

The Citadel in the center of Aleppo. This ancient land was shaped through the accumulation of conquerors in the region. This terrain represents, it is said, 5,000 years of history. This is a land of Abraham and the childhood home of Nazih Zuhdi.

Yousef Khanfar

# NAZIH ZUHDI
## FROM TIMELESS SANDS TO RED CLAY
## "HIS VISION BEYOND THE NEXT HORIZON"

Why did Nazih Zuhdi plant his roots in Oklahoma? With so many opportunities open to him, some people wonder what are the events that led his steps here. That is one of the most frequent questions that our scientist-heart surgeon hears. How did the son of a premiere Syrian ophthalmologist and an affluent Turkish mother from Istanbul find his way from the ancient Biblical lands to the red-clay heart of America? One way to answer the question would be with a litany of remarkable events and circumstances—a road map of serendipity from his birth city Beirut to Oklahoma City, his beloved chosen land. But for the deeply spiritual Dr. Zuhdi, one thought links them all. The answer, he says, is in the words which have become "a lamp unto my feet." Oklahoma, he believes, is the way appointed for Nazih Zuhdi—the destination for which God created him. "That says it all," relates Zuhdi. His Hand was always at work, bringing Zuhdi along the path to the place where He wanted him.

The way would begin with two cultured parents who prepared him for success—to expect it through the Mission Laique Française and subsequently the American University of Beirut (AUB). Zuhdi spent his first year at this unique oasis of learning, steeping himself in English and imbuing himself with the American vision. The young Zuhdi would create for himself an image of a country of limitless possibilities and a space for all his dreams. And while he was shaping his dreams, God was shaping him for a purpose. Along the road one would see his father Dr. Omar Zuhdi and AUB Dr. Mustafa Khaldi, who steered the young dreamer into medical school, and AUB Dr. Joseph McDonald, via Columbia University- Presbyterian Hospital, New York City, N.Y., who challenged him to be an investigative surgeon. Guided by his insatiable curiosity and a yetundefined craving, Zuhdi then crossed the ocean. He joined his dreams to the countless others who followed theirs, to the United States of America.

It is here, in July of 1950, in the United States, that God continues to mold a young man for a unique calling. In New York City, Zuhdi through St. Vincent Hospital at Staton Island, gained in 1951 his first taste of an experimental project at Columbia University-Presbyterian Hospital—"he had the opportunity to work with Dr. Arthur Voorhees who was developing synthetic vascular grafts as a circulatory medium"—as quoted by David Cooper in his book, *Open Heart*.

Then one would witness the intern-surgeon, learning the works of Dr. Clarence Dennis. They ignited his imagination, setting his curiosity ablaze with a vision of the potential of a heart-lung machine. Dennis then in 1953 would make his surgery resident a member of his research team at the State University of New York-Downstate Medical Center. His research consisted mainly of studies of variations of the rotating screen oxygenator and the Dale-Shuster pump. One of the originals of open-heart surgery with a heart-lung machine, Dr. John Kirklin asserted in 1991 that "Dr. Zuhdi has been working in the field of open-heart surgery virtually since its beginning ..."

From there Zuhdi moves in July of 1956 down his appointed path to the University of Minnesota, to the lean face of Dr. C. Walton Lillehei, the *King of Hearts*. Lillehei had advanced tremendously the discipline of open heart surgery, using a compatible person as a "pump-oxygenator" until his own Dewall-Lillehei Heart-Lung Machine was introduced successfully in July, 1955. Zuhdi was also assigned to study certain aspects of the Dewall-Lillehei Heart-Lung Machine and one of its derivitives, the sheet oxygenator. Later the master himself dubs Zuhdi a "master surgeon", and he, then at the fork in the road, advises Zuhdi to heed the "call" and take the train to Oklahoma City. From the moment in late 1957 when he steps off the train, Zuhdi felt that here at last are the wide-open spaces big enough to hold his dreams. At once his heart felt at home. He knew the immensity of the work ahead—the open prairies offered him the freedom to build on his dreams.

Zuhdi had learned the basics of the heart-lung machine from and with Clarence Dennis, and from C. Walton Lillehei had observed and studied a catalog of corrections of cardiac defects. Taken together, his two experiences made him uniquely qualified to usher in a totally new discipline of open-heart surgery in his research laboratories in the Sooner State. Here he would go further than his mentors had conceived for the third and critical piece of the surgical puzzle—his new principles of total body perfusion.

Once he arrives in Oklahoma for more than a fifty-year career and a life, there are so many names that emerge at just the right time to keep his heart here: Dr. John Schilling, who singled Zuhdi out for the University of Oklahoma; Dr. Allen Greer and Dr. John Carey, who became partners with him as new frontiers were forged; Sister Mary Coletta and Sister Mary Alvera at 13th Street Mercy Hospital Heart and Research Institute-Experimental Laboratory, who gave him the space to explore those frontiers; and John Kirkpatrick, who supplemented them in the finances of Zuhdi's laboratory that was his tools of discovery, along with his later moving Navy Lt. Commander Clark Ritchie to Oklahoma City from Washington, D.C., to assist Dr. Zuhdi in the development of an artificial bypass heart (1963-1965). At present, the Zuhdi-Ritchie Bypass Artificial Heart is the property of the Oklahoma History Center, an affiliate of the Smithsonian Institution.

Even little seven-year-old Terry Gene Nix stands tall as a vision from God. On February 25, 1960, at 13th Street Mercy Hospital, he would be the first patient to receive open-heart surgery with Dr. Zuhdi's "Total Intentional Hemodilution"—the first of millions worldwide to follow who would benefit from a whole new way of thinking. The principles of hemodilution apply not only to open-heart surgery but other disciplines, including transplantation. This in turn would be the beating heart of Oklahoma's gift to the world—recently calculated over half a century beginning in 1960 at an economic impact beyond eleven trillion dollars for open heart surgery itself...not to mention the nearly fifty million whom Total Intentional Hemodilution gave the chance for a better life. For many of those, it has meant life itself.

So many names, so many providential intersections mark the road: the Sisters of Mercy, Sister Mary Coletta, Sister Mary Alverra; Jay Henry, Kenneth Bonds, William Carpenter, Stanley Hupfeld, and Tom Lynn—who all in their own ways joined Zuhdi as he ushered in the new spirit of collaborative administration that became the heart of Mercy Hospital and Baptist Hospital of Oklahoma City.

"From the moment I stepped on these shores," explains Zuhdi, "my scientific curiosity and my research have drawn me irresistibly further into the American heartland. Nowhere else could I have done what I did here. Lebanon was my birthplace, but the journey has left me in the world of science." As the train that brought him to Oklahoma City chugged away, his feet, firm on the Rock Island and Pacific Railway platform, told him he was coming home. "For me, I was born a 'son of Abraham', and somehow I felt there were no strangers around me here. With friends gained, my feelings of family deepened."

This is where he became all he was born to be. A brief encounter at 13th Street Mercy Hospital in the sixties lingers in Zuhdi's mind and memory. One day an older man appeared before him, unfamiliar but imposing. He stopped Zuhdi, shook his hand, and looked him in the eye. He said simply,

"I am E.K. Gaylord. Stay. You are an Oklahoman." So Zuhdi was and so he is. Oklahoma was not only the open spaces in which he would grow his dreams; it was also the open heart that welcomed him, where his spirit could grow and flourish. Zuhdi finds his adopted nation still maturing as a 'model of modernism'—in science, in religion, in morality, in justice for all. "The world looks our way," Zuhdi asserts, "and sees a beacon shining bright with the possibilities of freedom and opportunity. Our nation is a nation still growing toward its calling—'to secure the blessings for our liberty for all and our moral integrity for all.'"

And this is where in the sixties, Sister Mary Alvera pointed out to him Annette McMichael, a young nursing student, and whispered, "Take her to dinner!" In 1970, they fulfilled both their destinies—becoming husband and wife as God had originally and gloriously planned. For over forty years Annette and Nazih Zuhdi have been two halves of one person. How did a young boy from Beirut and Aleppo, with ancient roots all the way back to Istanbul, settle in Oklahoma? How far back does God's hand mold the clay? The family tree of Sheyh Mestan of Macedonia, planted in 1457, has spread its leaves and branches, and Nazih Zuhdi's branch was destined to spread its shade over the plains of Oklahoma, and from there to the world. Becky Skidmore eloquently elaborated, "Zuhdi's life is a wave with an impact on the world…one stroke at a time." In the final telling, that's who he was in God's heart. "For every one of you God appointed a law and a way." This was the road made for him, and he was wonderfully made for that road. "God wills it."

# A WORD FROM A PERSPICACIOUS FRIEND

## THE MAN BEHIND THE MIRACLE

"There has to be a way."

Nazih Zuhdi, the man, is a human dynamo with seemingly endless energy and a passionate striving for perfection in every detail. As Dr. John Chaffin summarized, "many men have great dreams and many men perform great tasks. But few are both dreamers and doers. Nazih Zuhdi is that rare breed in both categories."

My wife Vicki and I know and love Nazih and Annette to the point that we have no closer friends in the world, and he is the head of a closely-knit family that does things together.

"There has to be a way," and it is found in his giant footsteps and beyond.

Vicki Clark Gourley,
Executive Editor and Publisher
*OKC Friday* Newspaper

J. Leland Gourley,
CEO, Editor and Publisher
*OKC Friday* Newspaper

# A WORD FROM A DISTINGUISHED HISTORIAN

For more than thirty years of my career I served as Executive Producer of the Oklahoma Hall of Fame Banquet and Induction Ceremony. This enabled me to meet and work with outstanding Oklahomans representing the sciences, business, the arts, sports, and volunteerism. In addition, most of those outstanding honorees were presented for induction by distinguished individuals from throughout the United States. Among those presenters were Henry Kissinger, Ronald Reagan, Bill Clinton, George H. W. Bush, Gerald Ford, Van Cliburn, and numerous other giants in their respective fields of endeavor. None of them made a greater impression on me than Dr. Nazih Zuhdi, who was inducted into the Oklahoma Hall of Fame in 1994. His remarkable accomplishments in medical science are well documented, but other aspects of his character may not be as widely recognized. His respect for people of all races, religious preferences, and occupations is universal, and he is one of the most generous individuals I have ever known. More than a half century ago, Dr. Zuhdi chose Oklahoma to be the place where he would live and work. There he repaired hearts through his revolutionary medical research and practice, and he won hearts through his love for people and for Oklahoma.

Paul F. Lambert
Membership and Development Director,
Oklahoma Historical Society

# A WORD FROM AN ESTEEMED COLLEAGUE

One of the pleasant privileges of serving with the Oklahoma Medical Board is meeting and interacting with doctors, both at the beginning of their careers and after they are well established. A high point of my 20-plus years here at the Medical Board has been making the acquaintance of and friendship with Dr. Zuhdi. He is an almost unbelievable combination of innovation, pride, enthusiasm, exuberance, and accuracy in the history of cardiovascular medicine and transplantation. Dr. Zuhdi performed the first Oklahoma heart transplant, March 4, 1985. Only after basking in the glow of Dr. Zuhdi's presence and conversation is it understandable how an intellectual import such as he has become the face of Oklahoma medicine to so many people—locally, nationally, and worldwide.

Gerald C. Zumwalt, M.D.
Secretary/Medical Board

If you look up the word "dignified" in the dictionary, there would be a picture of **Dr. Nazih Zuhdi.** He does not know how to lie, cheat, or steal. In other words he would be a dismal failure in politics, but as a heart surgeon/scientist he studied and trained with the best of those who came before him. Then he continued with his years of independent research. The medical world has climbed to loftier heights from his pioneering shoulders.

Max Edgar, Ph.D.
Psychologist

# A WORD FROM MY LUMINOUS DAUGHTER

What's a little girl to do when the most amazing man she will ever know is the very first one to hold her hand? Most people in Oklahoma City know that thousands of people owe their lives to the Nazih Zuhdi Transplant Center, but fewer may be aware of the greater millions his work has saved. He developed the principles and procedures of total intentional hemodilution—the deliberate priming of the heart-lung machine during surgery with something other than blood. This revolutionary step, originally scorned by many in the medical community, was nothing less than the democratization of open-heart surgery, making it safely available everywhere. Open heart surgeries went from an estimated 75 a day worldwide in 1960 to several thousand now. Over the last half-century that works out to millions of lives.

One of my earliest memories is as a daughter happily accompanying her father on Saturday morning rounds. This little girl learned so much on those rounds, lessons that shaped my life. He taught me compassion, not only in the way he cared for his patients, but also with the kindness and warmth he treated everyone he encountered, from janitor to chief executive. I also couldn't help but learn healthy habits as he preached preventive medicine. I was there as he blithely got his patients out of bed shortly after surgery to walk with him. He walked and walked. I also was recruited frequently to count laps in our brilliant blue pool for him. He has passed on to me a passion for exercise. He also taught me moderation in diet as well. "Never eat more of any food than will fit in an ice cream scoop!" Most of all, I remember his boundless optimism on those rounds. Life is so beautiful, do not worry and always live in hope.

I remember the light of love that was always shined on me and still is. My family's unconditional support is what makes me proudest, and my father's smile made me fearless. Many of my happiest memories are traveling with my family through diverse cultures around the world. I've survived earthquakes in Acapulco and been airlifted out of floods in South Africa. I've been humbled by the openness of people who seemingly have nothing. My father bestowed on me his boundless curiosity to see all that life has to offer. Most of all, my father's heart has instilled in me that a life is measured by what we give back to the world. Our blessings are not so much gifts as stewardships.

Quiet strength, elegance, compassion, graciousness, tolerance, love—all those, he has modeled for me. In the end, I have always known that I am his Nazette and he is, quite simply and gloriously, "Daddy!"

*Nazette Zuhdi*

Nazette Zuhdi

# A WORD FROM VIOLET

It was 1961, I had just entered Mercy School of Nursing. I had wanted to be a nurse since I was eight years old. I remember the first time I met Dr. Zuhdi. We were on a tour of the 5th floor, the Cardiac Unit at Mercy Hospital.

Dr. Zuhdi was on the floor making rounds, he stopped and spoke to us, the new students. He was very kind to us.

I was in fear and awe, as I had heard so much about the well known Heart Surgeon. Annette and I had been in Nursing School together and had been roommates and friends after graduation and worked on the Open Heart Surgery Team at Mercy Hospital. Little did I know that day, that I would eventually work with him on the Open Heart Surgery Team, become his Nurse and later the Recipient Heart & Lung Transplant Coordinator.

Thanks, Nazih for all you do and have done for me and all Mankind!

Today we remain dear friends, he, Annette and I.

*Violet T. Schlegel-Dyer*

2011 Violet T. Schlegel-Dyer

## A WORD FROM ROSE

My life has been greatly enriched
and blessed by Dr. Zuhdi and
Annette. I am a better person for
having known them.

*Rose*

Rose Lane
Editorial Assistant

Yousef Khanfar

Yousef Khanfar

*Above:* **The 13th Street Mercy Hospital in Oklahoma City where the landmark advances were performed between 1958-1965. The old building no longer exists, but the spirit has been transplanted into its new facilities 10 miles north.**
*Left:* **Nazih Zuhdi shrouded in memories that helped the world.**

Sister Mary Coletta, left,
and Sister Mary Alvera
opened the gates (1958-1963)
for Dr. Nazih Zuhdi,
Dr. Allen Greer, and
Dr. John Carey to make
possible all that followed.

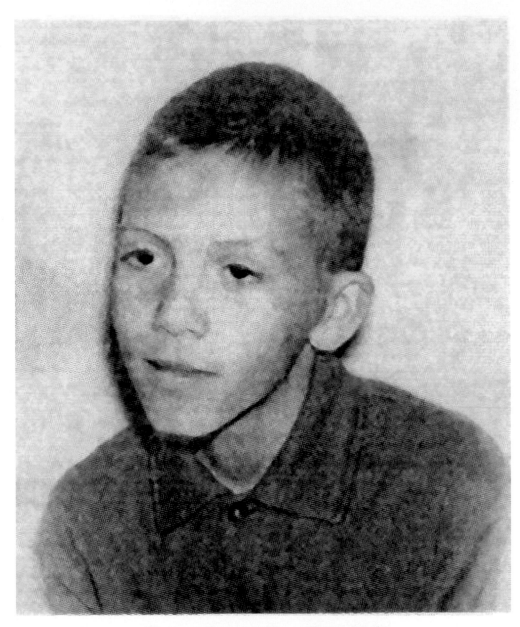

**Terry Gene Nix, 1953-1963**
"The First in the World"
Total Intentional Hemodilution performed on February 25, 1960
13th Street Mercy Hospital, Oklahoma City, Oklahoma

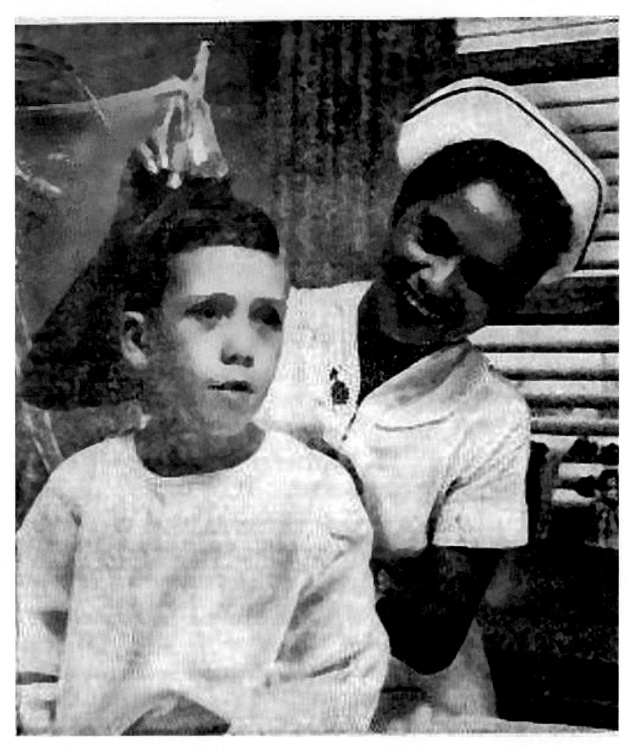

A story in *The Daily Oklahoman* on February 28, 1960 read, "Terry Gene Nix, 7, of Broken Bow, Oklahoma, gets his hair combed by nurse Ida Bearhead Neiswanger, following his historic role in Mercy's open-heart surgery procedure." With an enigmatic smile that shines even today, Ida Bearhead Neiswanger claims she made Zuhdi famous by her watchful, meticulous care of Terry. Of course, she concedes, "Zuhdi helped." *Courtesy Oklahoma Publishing Company.*

Even the gift of Life does not last forever.

Terry Gene Nix's historic surgery granted him another 3-and-a-half years of childhood before Ewing's Sarcoma, a bone tumor unrelated to his heart surgery, claimed him.

He blazed a trail for millions of people who have never heard his name.

The courage of Terry Gene Nix and his contribution to medical science was never forgotten by Dr. Nazih Zuhdi. A monument was placed at Nix's gravesite in the Alva, Oklahoma, Community Cemetery on September 23, 2011. The simple but elegant monument commemorated the first open-heart surgery performed while using Dr. Zuhdi's pioneering technique of Total Intentional Hemodilution of the blood. Nix, a brave seven-year-old boy, truly was "the Gateway to All," because total hemodilution of the blood made open-heart surgery possible on a massive scale, thereby saving the lives of millions during the ensuing decades.

Some of the visitors to Alva, Friday, September 23, 2011 to participate in the special memorial for Terry Gene Nix were relatives and others were from Oklahoma City, associates of Dr. Nazih Zuhdi, the physician who honored the contribution to the health of millions of people around the world made by Nix. Pictured above from the left are: Shelly Crynes with the Oklahoma Historical Society; Glendelle Nix (a 2nd cousin); Sister Miriam Terese Alvarado; Sister Rose Elizabeth Power, both of Mercy Health Center in Oklahoma City; Gini Moore Campbell with the Oklahoma Heritage Association; Dr. Nazih Zuhdi; Sariene Stauffer (a 2nd cousin); Paul F. Lambert with Oklahoma Historical Society; Justin Beadles and Bill Wandel (not in picture) with INTEGRIS Hospital in Oklahoma City.

*Photo and story by Roger McKenzie of* Alva Review-Courier *September 27, 2011.*

## Marker here memorializes the life saving contribution of Terry Gene Nix

*Roger McKenzie; published in the September 27, 2011, issue of the* Alva Review-Courier, *Alva, Ok.*

A brief but moving ceremony Friday marked the installation and dedication of a marker placed at the grave of a 10-year-old boy buried in Alva Municipal Cemetery next to his mother. The marker noted the contribution of Terry Gene Nix, who in 1960 at the age of seven underwent open heart surgery using, for the first time ever, total intentional hemodilution.

Now the standard of care used everywhere for open heart surgery, the procedure was developed by Dr. Nazih Zuhdi and his team at Mercy Hospital in Oklahoma City. In the years since Dr. Zuhdi and his team first used it when he repaired the heart of the young boy, the procedure has made open heart surgery readily available around the world and has saved millions of lives.

The marker was placed at the request of Dr. Zuhdi, who attended the ceremony along with relatives of Terry Nix and representatives of Mercy Hospital and Integris Baptist Hospital, as well as Oklahoma Historical Society and Oklahoma Heritage Association members.

The brave young boy and the medical pioneer combined to make history. Friday's ceremony will leave a permanent reminder that even the least of us can have a great impact on the entire world.

# PIONEERING HEART PATIENT HONORED FIVE DECADES LATER

*John A. Small, News Editor; published in the Sept. 9, 2011, issue of the*
Johnston County Capital-Democrat, *Tishomingo, OK*

The son of a Johnston County couple who was the first person to undergo a type of open heart surgery is being honored by the surgeon who performed the operation half a century ago.

Terry Gene Nix, the son of Opal and Robbi Nix of Tishomingo, was 7 years old on Feb. 25, 1960, when Dr. Nazih Zuhdi performed the first Total Intentional Hemodilution heart surgery ever performed on a human.

The operation was a success and paved the way for the saving of countless lives; however, young Terry died three years later from complications from another unrelated illness.

Robbi Nix told the Capital-Democrat last week that she was recently contacted by Dr. Zuhdi, who told her of plans to erect a special monument at her son's gravesite in Alva, commemorating Terry's place in medical history.

"It's a granite marker placed in front of the gravestone," Mrs. Nix said last Thursday. "It's in place now, but we haven't gotten to go see it yet. We're going to try to go see it some time in October." Nix said the new marker, placed at Dr. Zuhdi's expense, reads as follows:

> *Terry Gene Nix*
> *The Gateway to All*
> *Total Intentional Hemodilution*
> *By Whom Millions Have Come To Life*
> *February 25, 1960*
> *Remembrance by Nazih Zuhdi, M.D.*

Terry was 20 months old when a seemingly routine doctor's visit led to a terrible discovery: the boy's heart was failing him.

"We were living in Broken Bow at the time," Mrs. Nix recalled. "We thought he had a cold, but the doctor found out he had a heart murmur. That's what they called it back then."

From that point Terry endured countless doctor visits before he was finally referred to Dr. Wiley McCollum at Mercy Hospital in Oklahoma City.

McCollum had established the first cardiac catheterization laboratory in a community hospital in Oklahoma capable of producing images of the heart.

While the technology was a far cry to that available today, at the time it offered the best possible view into the human heart. McCollum was able to identify the specific defect and diagnosed Terry with pulmonary valvular stenosis—a narrowing of the valve controlling the flow of blood through the heart and lungs.

The defect had caused the youngster's heart to become overworked, dramatically decreasing the flow of oxygen. Surgery was the only option, but McCollum advised the family to postpone it as long as possible, to allow the medical community time to learn more about the condition.

But as time went by Terry's condition worsened, and his parents feared that time was running out. Finally it was determined that Terry was an ideal candidate for the procedure which Zuhdi had coined, studied and perfected.

A native of Beirut, Lebanon, Zuhdi had already spent a number of years in the field of study that led to Terry's landmark operation. From 1952 to 1956 he worked at the Brooklyn Center under doctors Clarence Dennis, Karl Karlson and Charles Fries, who had built an early pumpoxygenator.

After working with Fries on several re-designs of Dennis' original model, Zuhdi moved to the University of Minnesota to work with Dr. C. Walton Lillehei, who had designed his own version of a cross-circulation heart-lung machine. Zuhdi's work at UM centered around solving the problem of air bubbles while bypassing the heart, so the heart could be stopped for surgery.

In 1957 Zuhdi moved to Oklahoma City and, with doctors Allen Greer and John Carey, formed a three-man open heart surgery team. He also continued his efforts to improve on Lillehei's heart-lung machine; in addition to being smaller, Zuhdi's device included modifications that, among other things, reduced the need for blood to a minimal amount and reduced the prep time from two hours to 20 minutes.

Zuhdi's procedure, known as Total Intentional Hemodilution, was said to have been conceived and perfected in his laboratory at the Mercy Heart and Research Institute in 1959. But it wasn't until he and the Nix family were brought together that the procedure would be used on a human being.

Although the family and referring physician had granted consent for the operation, Zuhdi wanted Terry's blessing as well before proceeding. According to a biographical article about Zuhdi written by Gini Moore Campbell, the surgeon sat down next to Terry on his bed and explained the procedure in detail.

Zuhdi reportedly ending his explanation by winking and telling Terry, "All will go well and you'll be famous." According to Campbell, Terry's response was, "Let's go for it!"

The surgery lasted three hours and required only 1.5 pints of banked blood to replace that lost in surgery – not the fresh gallons especially prepared for previous open heart surgeries. After surgery Terry was sent to recovery and, just a day later, was smiling for newspaper cameras.

It was the first of several history-making projects that Zuhdi would be a part of during his career. Later in 1963, while still at the Mercy Heart and Research Institute, Zuhdi and Commander Clark Ritchie of the U.S. Navy developed a precursor to the artificial bypass hearts commonly used today.

In 1985 Zuhdi performed Oklahoma's first heart transplant at Baptist Hospital, where he later also performed other medical milestones such as the first heart-lung transplant, the first single lung transplant, the first left ventricular by-pass artifical heart, the first right ventricular by-pass artifical heart and the first double-lung transplant. [He also initiated and founded an abdominal organ transplant division and the corrsponding medical components.]

In November of 1984 he founded the Oklahoma Transplant Institute. It was renamed in August of 1999 the Nazih Zuhdi Transplant Institute. Comprised of physicians and surgeons from all specialties, the one-of-a-kind facility at that time was a complete interdisciplinary transplantation center for all solid organs.

In 1961 the Nix family moved to Tishomingo, but shortly afterward Terry found himself faced with another health crisis. He was diagnosed with Ewing's Sarcoma, a bone tumor unrelated to the heart defect; the tumor resulted in Terry's death three and a half years after the surgery that made him and his doctor famous.

Bobbi Nix remembers her son as a "sweet and compassionate and brave child" who always thought of others.

While he was too young to fully grasp the impact his experience would have on the medical world, Terry Gene Nix's 1960 operation opened the door for the saving of literally millions of lives in the years that have followed.

Those lives are Terry's legacy. Half a century later, the doctor who made it possible has seen to it that this legacy is never forgotten.

# A WORD FROM BOB BURKE

Dr. Zuhdi's is the only medical research conducted within the boundaries of Oklahoma that is recognized in the first edition, 1968, of World Who's Who in Science: A Biographical Dictionary of Notable Scientists from Antiquity to the Present, a leading publication edited by Allen G. Debus, then Professor of History of Science at the University of Chicago, his colleagues, and an advisory council representing 20 of the most respected institutions in the field of science.

The story of Dr. Zuhdi's pioneering research, surgeries, and transplants appears in the book alongside biographical sketches of historic scientists such as Galileo, Sir Isaac Newton, Louis Pasteur, Albert Einstein, Charles Darwin, and Thomas Edison. It is noted that Dr. Zuhdi's hemodilution technique was used by Dr. Christiaan Barnard in the world's first human heart transplant.

Bob Burke
Attorney, Author & Historian

# "THOSE WERE THE DAYS"—before the year 2000

## In that period of time, 1958-1965, "All Paths Led to Oklahoma City."
**from** *The Life of Nazih Zuhdi: Uncharted Voyage of a Heart*

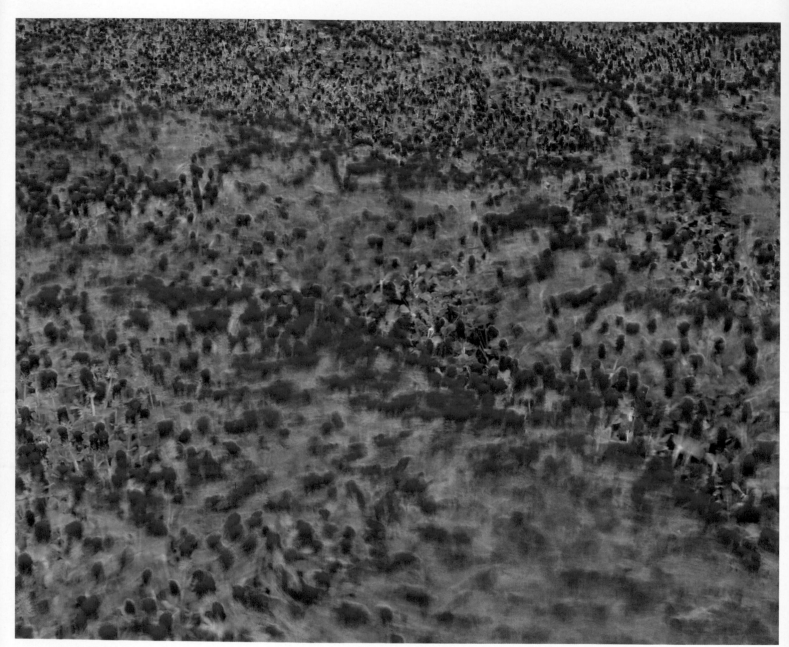

Yousef Khanfar

# CONTEMPLATIONS

Nazih Zuhdi's introduction of the use of a nonhemic prime producing Total Intentional Hemodilution was one of the truly revolutionary advances in the medical science of experimental and clinical open-heart surgery. In January, 1959, physiologist Frank Gollan expressed his doubts about the feasibility of hemodilution beyond a very limited use in a review article in the *Journal of the Michigan State Medical Society*: "…Dilution of blood with **Ringer's** Solution to a hematocrit of about 35 percent would seem a priori to be an objectionable or even dangerous step since hemoglobin and plasma proteins are temporarily reduced to unphysiological levels … However, blood volumes studies with radioactive iodinated albumen indicate that the entire volume of the less viscous, diluted blood is available for the artificial circulation …" Gollan's statement seemed to vindicate the normothermic czars of the then established protocol for open-heart surgery.

The gateway that unleashed the liberating effect of Zuhdi's Total Intentional Hemodilution would be available to all. After hearing of Zuhdi's work, Gollan summarized, with a touch of awe, the wider effect of the physiological principles of Total Intentional Hemodilution for open-heart surgery when he wrote to him in December 26, 1960, a scant few months after the first reports of Zuhdi's accomplishments, "…but to dilute the blood to such an extent in a human being was a different matter and I did not think that anybody would do it because it was against our conditioned reflexes as physicians. Of course, I am very gratified that you did so successfully…"

These "conditioned reflexes" were vividly demonstrated by the meticulous avoidance of any hemodilution and they were very amusing to Zuhdi. Dr. Herbert Warden, in a telephone communication to Zuhdi, indicated that he divided open-heart surgery into two eras, the pre-Zuhdi era and the post-Zuhdi era. Chapter 6 in my book *The Life of Nazih Zuhdi: Uncharted Voyage of a Heart* is a revelatory reading of that period of time.

Yousef Khanfar

# REFLECTIONS

If the blessings of liberty are to be secured for all people, certain fundamental rights must be honored. A man is not free if his belly rumbles, shakes, and shouts from hunger. The Oklahoman recently reported, Pope Benedict XVI told delegates of the UN Food and Agricultural Organization that access to food is a basic human right that must be guaranteed. He said it is urgent to develop economic models that are not just based on profit but take into account "the human dimension." "How can we remain silent when even food has become the object of speculation or is linked to a market that, without any regulation and deprived of moral principles, appears linked solely to an objective of profit? High food prices require an international response to uphold the dignity of all people." In the face of such global concerns, what can one person do? How can my concern reach over the waters and speed across a continent to free a child from the shackles of hunger? It begins with an idea, an idea that food transcends the demands of greed that encompasses so much that we believe. It begins with one voice saying, "There is another way," and passing that vision on to another. Bill T Jones, recently honored at the Kennedy Center, expressed it through the medium he knew best: "Art is a participation in the world of ideas. A loaf of bread feeds a family of four; an idea feeds the minds of a million people."

Equally fundamental to hunger is health. Just as the access to food is guaranteed, so must the access to health care be guaranteed as well. But health care is more than a product, like food. It is a skill that must be learned and acquired. It is ideas in their purest form, implanted in the human mind and applied in the human body. It must be love made manifest and passed on...freely. Nazih Zuhdi, through his life and career, has embraced this idea. Total Intentional Hemodilution—the priming of the heart-lung machine during open heart surgery, making it both safe and affordable—was a revolution in cardiac care. The economic impact of his work was recently calculated at over eleven trillion dollars. A man is entitled to the profits of his labors, but Zuhdi's insights and methods were his gift to the world. Freely they came to Oklahoma City; freely he taught them; freely they learned, and the benefits of Total Intentional Hemodilution flowed freely everywhere.

An old Chinese proverb says, "Give a man a fish, he eats for a day; teach him to fish, and he eats for a lifetime." Zuhdi taught, and fed not only minds, but the hearts and lives of millions. That has been the gift of Oklahoma "to uphold the dignity of all people."

Yousef Khanfar

Dr. Zuhdi's career represents a rare combination of clinical wisdom, scientific brilliance, compassion for others and the powerful will to cut through obstacles like Alexander's sword cut the Gorgon's knot. It has been a rare privilege to know and work for him. Like Tennyson's Ulysses, he always roamed with a hungry heart, sought knowledge like a star and remained strong in will to strive and seek.

David P. Nelson, MD
Chief, Heart Transplant Medicine
Nazih Zuhdi Transplant Institute
INTEGRIS Baptist Medical Center

Dr. Nelson was not even a speck in his parents' eyes when **Dr. Zuhdi** was doing his major work. **Dr. Zuhdi** and **Dr. Nelson** worked together so long that Nelson grew to be a pillar within NZTI and was an integral factor in securing **Dr. James Long** and ensuring the continued progress of the Institute.

Like the motion of the sea, time moves on inexorably, washing away beaches and reshaping shorelines. But every once in a great while comes along someone whose footprints are imprinted so deep that the tides cannot wash them away. In fact, the passage of the years serves only to wear away the inconsequential and trivial, so that the impression of his passing stands ever starker and ever bolder.

I believe this image describes the legacy of one Oklahoman— Dr. Nazih Zuhdi. Uncounted millions are alive today because his work revolutionized open-heart surgery.

Zuhdi's principles of Total Intentional Hemodilution (TIHD) made that surgery available on a scale undreamed of by its earliest visionaries— and its translation into all variations and derivatives of bloodless surgery. This work, at the 13th Street Mercy Hospital Heart and Research Institute— Experimental Laboratory, chaired by Nazih Zuhdi, was founded and funded by Allen Greer, John Carey, and Nazih Zuhdi, Inc. and Mercy Hospital. John Kirkpatrick was a crucial facilitator. During this period of time several crucial dimensions of total body perfusion including a cell saver were designed, experimentally proven (1957-1960), clinically applied (February 25, 1960), and published.

So it is fitting that, just as the waters of earth erode away the sediments to reveal its secrets, so do the swirls and eddies of the decades move to reveal new evidence of Zuhdi's unparalleled contribution to humanity.

In 1991 Zuhdi was nominated for the Distinguished Scientist Award presented by the American College of Cardiology. Through the grace and kindness of Zuhdi's friend, his former scientist-in-residence, and his colleague, Professor David Cooper of the University of Pittsburgh, who had a definite role in Zuhdi's superior heart transplant program at NZTI, those letters of nomination have recently resurfaced nearly twenty years after they were written. They are extraordinary documents written by extraordinary men—the men who carved the very foundations of open-heart surgery. Drs. Clarence Dennis, (Dennis refers to Zuhdi as a "co-worker" in that period of time), C. Walton Lillehei, (Lillehei refers to Zuhdi as a "Master Surgeon"), John Kirklin, and Richard DeWall (DeWall and Zuhdi were co-trainees of Lillehei) are all giants in the field, and in these letters they affirm that Dr. Nazih Zuhdi is a foundation to the final solution—Zuhdi's Total Intentional Hemodilution, total body perfusion, open-heart surgery and bloodless surgery and all medical and surgical derivatives.

Yousef Khanfar

The 1991 letters of nomination of Dr. Nazih Zuhdi for the "Distinguished Scientist Award" of the American College of Cardiology are only part of a historic panoramic landscape— Zuhdi was already included in the "Milestones of Cardiovascular Medicine" of the American College of Cardiology—1628-1989. Dr. Zuhdi glows with honor and an overwhelming sense of gratitude that such giant pioneers in the field would be moved to endorse him.

Yousef Khanfar

 **SCHOOL OF MEDICINE**

*The following letter was scanned in its entirety.*

Department of Surgery
Division of Cardiothoracic Surgery

August 14, 1991

American College of Cardiology
Scientific Awards Committee
Heart House
9111 Old Georgetown Road
Bethesda, Maryland   20814

Dear Colleagues:

I am writing in support of the nomination of Dr. Nazih Zuhdi, of
Oklahoma City, Oklahoma, for a Distinguished Scientist Award by
the American College of Cardiology.

Dr. Zuhdi has been working in the field of open heart surgery
virtually since its beginning. His major contributions were made
quite a long time ago, and therefore today seem almost
conventional wisdom. However, it is Dr. Zuhdi who introduced the
use of hemodilution, one of the very fundamental aspects of
cardiopulmonary bypass today. He has made other contributions as
well, but this one alone would qualify him for the award of
Distinguished Scientist, in my opinion.

Thank you for considering him for this distinguished award.

Sincerely,

John W. Kirklin, M.D.
Professor of Surgery
Division of Cardiothoracic Surgery

JWK:ae

The University of Alabama at Birmingham
780 Lyons-Harrison Research Building • 1919 Seventh Avenue South • UAB Station
Birmingham, Alabama 35294-0007 • (205) 934-5167 • FAX (205) 934-2055

## SUPPORTING THE NOMINATION

John Kirklin, one of the original pioneers in the field of open-heart surgery, strongly supported the nomination of Dr. Nazih Zuhdi for the American College of Cardiology's Distinguished Scientist Award. His is the first of four letters that are published in this book.

On June 30, 1955, a survey by Clarence Dennis counted only six successful open-heart surgeries done with a heart-lung machine. Four were performed by Dr. John Kirklin of the Mayo Clinic in Rochester, Minn., (the first on March 22, 1955) at that time using a Modified Gibbon heart-lung machine. The other two were performed by John Gibbon at Jefferson Medical College, Philadelphia, Pa. (May 6, 1953) and Clarence Dennis at the State University of New York-Downstate Medical Center (June 30, 1955)—both successful. Nazih Zuhdi performed the first open-heart surgery with Total Intentional Hemodilution at 13th Street Mercy Hospital, Oklahoma City, Ok., on February 25, 1960—successful.

However, to be added to the list of six (1953-June 30, 1955) is Viking Bjork, of Sweden; he performed a successful open-heart surgery with a heart-lung machine—July 16, 1954.

C. Walton Lillehei, University of Minnesota, performed his first cross-circulation, using a compatible human being as a heart lung machine, on March 26, 1954—successful.

Yousef Khanfar

# Birth of Open Heart Surgery Between April 5, 1951-July 12, 1955
## Including November 1, 1954—the FIRST Human Case of Mechanical
## Assistance to a Failing Heart *and* Nazih Zuhdi through 1960

In the following, the steps that Nazih Zuhdi took involved
primarily the pioneers of the United States of America.

April 5, 1951 Clarence Dennis, University of Minnesota, Minneapolis, Minnesota, USA,
open heart surgery with heart-lung machine UNSUCCESSFUL

September 2, 1952 John Lewis, University of Minnesota, Minneapolis, Minnesota, USA,
open-heart surgery with external hypothermia SUCCESSFUL

FIRST successful open heart surgery with heart-lung machine in the world.
May 6, 1953 John Gibbon, Jefferson Medical College, Philadelphia, Pennsylvania,
USA open heart surgery with heart-lung machine SUCCESSFUL

March 26, 1954 C. Walton Lillehei, University of Minnesota, Minneapolis, Minnesota,
USA, open heart surgery with cross-circulation SUCCESSFUL

July 16, 1954, Viking Bjork, Sabbatsberg Hospital, Stockholm, Sweden, open heart surgery
with heart-lung machine SUCCESSFUL

FIRST Mechanical Assistance to a Failing Heart in the world. November 1, 1954 Clarence
Dennis, State University of New York—Downstate Medical Center, Brooklyn, New York,
USA, SUCCESSFUL. Zuhdi was a contributing member of the team and Dennis coined him
"co-worker." (See page 105.)

March 22, 1955 John Kirklin, Mayo Clinic, Rochester, Minnesota, USA, open heart surgery
with heart-lung machine SUCCESSFUL

May 13, 1955 C.Walton Lillehei, University of Minnesota, Minneapolis, Minnesota, USA,
open heart surgery with heart-lung machine UNSUCCESSFUL

FIRST open heart surgery with the heart-lung machine in the State of New York, second east
of the Mississippi River, and sixth in the nation. June 30, 1955 Clarence Dennis, State University
of New York—Downstate Medical Center, Brooklyn, New York, USA, SUCCESSFUL.

July 12, 1955 C.Walton Lillehei, University of Minnesota, Minneapolis, Minnesota, USA,
open heart surgery with heart-lung machine SUCCESSFUL

FIRST open heart surgery with TOTAL INTENTIONAL HEMODILUTION.
February 25, 1960 Nazih Zuhdi, 13th Street Mercy Hospital, Oklahoma City, Oklahoma,
USA, SUCCESSFUL.

Yousef Khanfar

**Only two things are infinite
the UNIVERSE, and human stupidity**

Albert Einstein
(1879-1955)

**Amateurs think strategy.
Professionals think logistics.**

General Omar Bradley
(1893-1981)

As recalled by David Cooper, Nazih Zuhdi's opinion was,

"Every man has a moment in life when God permits him to touch the sky."

If you do not know that you do not know, that is a calamity to reality.

Massaging the truth "is a point of no return."

Integrity and dignity should never be for sale.

Dr. Nazih Zuhdi

July, 1956. There was a new atmosphere into which Nazih Zuhdi entered fresh from his preparation for his American Board of Surgery certification in the summer of 1956, and it would have profound influence on the young surgeon. Zuhdi had done his residency in surgery under Clarence Dennis, but his passion was also in the laboratory, where he learned the rudiments of the heart-lung machine. With C. Walton Lillehei he would not only continue to pursue his evolving interest in the machine and new dimensions of perfusion physiology; he would also learn Lillehei's pioneering procedures for treating a wide variety of heart defects. One common quality linked both endeavors—Zuhdi remained in the very cauldron of innovation, working side by side to forge the origins of a new discipline of the heart.

Until June 30, 1955 the focus of the two groups, Clarence Dennis and John Gibbon, then pursuing the Grail of open-heart surgery, was to find a workable heart-lung machine. Lillehei bypassed the problem by "cross-circulation"—the first cross-circulation case was performed by Lillehei on March 16, 1954—the use of another live compatible human being as the patient's "pump-oxygenator" during open-heart surgery. Through this elegant solution, Lillehei brilliantly addressed the heart defects themselves while others were still struggling to find a reliable means. When the rest of the medical world combined could account only six successful open-heart surgeries of the simplest kind, Lillehei himself had accomplished 45 across a range of defects. Thus, he justly earned the title, "King of Hearts." The methodology of cross-circulation was abandoned around June 1955 with the first successful case with the Dewall-Lillehei bubble oxygenator on July 12, 1955.

And thus, Zuhdi would become a total heart surgeon, learning from the master himself how to think, cut, mend, and sew in and around the human heart. Zuhdi augmented his already prodigious surgical skills. With Lillehei and his other fellows, Zuhdi moved easily back and forth between clinic and the laboratory with a fluidity that would later characterize Zuhdi's own work in Oklahoma City. Zuhdi was a member of the throng as a fellow, and in that assembly of the brightest and most passionate—Richard Dewall, Norman Shumway, Mathias Paneth, William Weirich, Vincent Gott, and Christiaan Barnard—Zuhdi floated up to a rarefied atmosphere of knowledge and skill. Within two months of his arrival, Lillehei was writing to his Chief Wangensteen an internal memo that described the young Zuhdi as "brilliant." As Lillehei would later say, "this proved to be a very prescient observation." Zuhdi scrubbed and observed and assisted in surgeries in both the research laboratory and the operating theatre. Aglass wall rimmed the operating room above. Visitors from around the world could sit in "the dome" and observe the procedures that Lillehei was developing. Such a setting created something of the spirit of a momentous festival of significance, an atmosphere of excitement and important discovery.

Zuhdi approached the completion of his traineeship with the master, Lillehei. After a day of surgery, Lillehei had sat on a bench with his pupil, put his arm around his shoulder, and told him, "Remember, you can do it all."

From the seminal pioneer Clarence Dennis, Zuhdi had earned the designation of "co-worker" in the early development of the heart-lung machine. Now, the master himself, Lillehei, anointed Zuhdi as "a master surgeon." Mentored by both titans, Dennis and Lillehei. Zuhdi was ready to conquer any real world. But Zuhdi knew that for the kind of research he envisioned as the next step, he needed neither the support nor the restrictions of a traditional institution. He would design a laboratory, custom fit to his own quest—not trim his sights to existing horizons. He would not only conquer the world; he would create one...in Oklahoma.

*Photograph by Jim Meeks, Curator of the Oklahoma History Center.*

## THE DOUBLE HELIX

Zuhdi, lower left, modified the Dewall-Lillehei Heart-Lung Machine by inserting his stainless steel coil through the helix of the oxygenator to regulate the temperature of the blood with water from the brand-new garbage cans used as containers.

In 2005, a team of Mercy Hospital engineers, Dwight Shrum and Charles Hawkins, produced from Zuhdi's original papers this replica of the 1959-1960 machine.

This "Double-Helix" reduced the amount of priming blood and led Zuhdi to conceive his Total Intentional Hemodilution. That, later referred to as "Zuhdi's Double Vision," opened the gates in every nook and cranny of the entire world for open-heart surgery.

The Sigmamotor Pump of New York was the only pump used experimentally and clinically by Zuhdi at that time. He had studied it thoroughly when he was a trainee of C. Walton Lillehei, University of Minnesota, who used it for all his experimental and clinical work.

The first clinical application of Total Intentional Hemodilution was by Nazih Zuhdi, Allen Greer, John Carey, John Montroy, Wiley McCollum, Modine Pierce, Betty Blackburn, Mary Spencer, Peggy Johnson, Ida Bearhead, Florene Wallace and Sister Mary Alvera was on February 25, 1960 in Operating Room 5 at 13th Street Mercy Hospital in Oklahoma City, Oklahoma.

All future heart-lung machines incorporate Nazih Zuhdi's physiologic principles.

In the background of the photograph is the Zuhdi-Ritchie By-Pass Artificial Heart of 1964.

**TOP PHOTOGRAPH:** Nazih Zuhdi with the replica of the heart-lung machine that changed the world of open heart surgery and total body perfusion—Zuhdi's Total Intentional Hemodilution. The top photograph is with his wife Annette, who was with him as a student nurse, as was Vi McAuliff (not pictured), helping in the experimental laboratory.

**LOWER PHOTOGRAPH:** Nazih Zuhdi with Dan Provo, Director of the Oklahoma History Center. Provo's responsibility is to maintain the standards of excellence and accuracy that secure the Oklahoma History Center's affiliation with the Smithsonian Institution.

PHOTOGRAPHS BY JIM MEEKS, CURATOR OF EXHIBITS, OKLAHOMA HISTORY CENTER, 800 NAZIH ZUHDI DRIVE, OKLAHOMA CITY, OKLAHOMA: Nazih Zuhdi's double helical reservoir heart-lung machine, a Zuhdi modification of the DeWall-Lillehei Heart-Lung Machine, which brought about Zuhdi's final solution to total body perfusion open-heart surgery and bloodless surgery into reality—1957-1960.

Yousef Khanfar

Cell savers of different names and designs
have been used from the early 1950s in
open-heart surgery, experimentally and clinically
on millions and millions and millions
of people. One such device was part of the
work at the 13th Street Mercy Hospital
Heart and Research Institute in 1959.

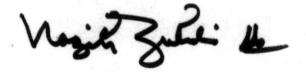

**Yousef Khanfar**

# THE BIRTH OF OPEN-HEART SURGERY

## The Story of the Heart Lung Machine, Total Body Perfusion and All Its Derivatives, Total Intentional Hemodilution Bloodless Surgery

## The Path Taken By Nazih Zuhdi

## 1952-1956
## 1957-1960
## One by One, the Pieces of the Perfusions Fell into Place For the Whole World, For All

Heart Lung Machine
Clarence Dennis, John Gibbon
1950 - June 30, 1956
**Zuhdi** was designated a
"co-worker" by Dennis
(1953).

Cross Circulation—C. Walton Lillehei
Heart Lung Machine and Clinical
Corrective Catalogue of Heart Defects
C. Walton Lillehei and John Kirklin
1954-1956
**Zuhdi** was a "trainee" of Lillehei
(July 1, 1956 - December 30, 1956).

**The Foundation of the Solution**
**Total Body Perfusion**
**Total Intentional Hemodilution**
**Nazih Zuhdi—Experimental**
**Research In Continuum**
**(1957-1960)**

# THE WORLD OF HEART LUNG MACHINES AND OPEN HEART SURGERY AND DERIVATIVES
## THE SINGULAR PATH OF NAZIH ZUHDI
## TO THE SOLUTION OF TOTAL BODY PERFUSION
THE SEMINAL PIONEERS, THE GUIDING LIGHTS WHO CARVED OUT ZUHDI'S PATH
OF HEART-LUNG MACHINES, AND OPEN HEART SURGERY.
CLARENCE DENNIS, (1909-2005), JOHN GIBBON, (1903-1973), JOHN KIRKLIN, (1917-1994),
C. WALTON LILLEHEI, (1918-1999), AND NAZIH ZUHDI, (1925- ).
THESE ARE THE BOLD VOICES THAT LED OPEN-HEART SURGERY OUT OF THE WILDERNESS

**JULY 1, 1952-JUNE 30, 1955**

Date chosen by Clarence Dennis for all that happened before

**JULY 1, 1952-DECEMBER 31, 1956**

Zuhdi was a "co-worker" of the early group at the State University of New York—Downstate Medical Center, Brooklyn, New York, with the titan pioneer of pump-oxygenators, Clarence Dennis. Zuhdi believes he was the only "co-worker" at that time who also became a trainee at the Cardiovascular service of the "King of Hearts", C. Walton Lillehei at the University of Minnesota, Minneapolis, Minnesota. Lillehei followed the path of mending the various heart defects using "cross-circulation"—a compatible human as a pump oxygenator; followed later by DeWall-Lillehei bubble oxygenator. Zuhdi was also assigned some experimental investigations of the DeWall-Lillehei Heart-Lung Machine and its Sheet version.

**1957-1960**

Charles Fries, a "co-worker" of Clarence Dennis, visited Zuhdi's laboratories in 1960 for a week at 13th Street Mercy Hospital, Oklahoma City, Oklahoma and this is a rendition of his visit: In the final analysis, he said, any number of mechanical alternatives might have worked. In retrospect, Fries lamented, "The team never did get good at performing the procedure or even get a chance to get used to one edition of the machine. It was not always the machine's fault."
Today Zuhdi himself believes some of the variations of the machine used during that period would have performed well if his present-day principles of Total Intentional Hemodilution and Total Body Perfusion had been applied during the perfusion process. Fries has commented on Zuhdi's observations, "You were right of course. We spent much too little time perfecting our perfusion and surgical skills. If the dog died, we spent the next week or weeks modifying the machine."

Concurrently with his basic studies of hypothermic perfusion and with his diminishment of the circuitry, Zuhdi, like all others in the field, was frustrated by the inadequacies of total body perfusion with blood prime and the complexities of obtaining fresh, heparinized blood. The problem was exacerbated in a small community hospital in Oklahoma City, and he began to investigate the traditionally banned use of banked citrated blood in open-heart surgery. Blood banks routinely added citrate to their blood supplies to prevent clotting. But Clarence Dennis had reported the first instance of possible citrate poisoning during his clinical, unsuccessful open-heart surgery in 1951, the first in the world. J. Bunker, in his report on "Citric Acid Intoxication" at the Sixth Congress of the International Society of Blood Transfusion in 1956, stated that citrated blood should not be used in open-heart surgery or hypothermia because of the danger of such poisoning. In addition, he cited concerns about the added volume of fluid which blood so treated would add to the perfusion system. His pronouncement summarized the then current conventional medical wisdom and underlined the prevailing resistance to any dilution of the blood during open-heart surgery. However, Zuhdi believed, as did Dennis later, that multiple factors entered the picture, and such conclusions might not be warranted.

Zuhdi's laboratory experiments in mid-1959 demonstrated the efficacy and safety of citrated blood in priming the heart-lung machine and for blood loss replacement if needed. Routinely collected citrated and processed banked blood up to five days old was used successfully to prime his modification of the DeWall-Lillehei extracorporeal system — a step that dramatically increased the practicality and the safety of open-heart procedures.

Zuhdi eventually expanded the window for viability to eight days. He and his colleagues described the results in an article submitted to Anesthesiology on January 2, 1960, and published in the September-October issue of that year. The delay of the paper's publication signaled the incomprehensible audacity of Zuhdi's concept for the blood necessary for open heart surgery. Zuhdi summarizes: "Freshly drawn heparinized blood had been advocated at that time for open heart surgery; fresh to secure the least altered blood and heparinized to avoid citrate poisoning and overloading with fluids. However, citrated-banked blood obtained in routine fashion, following Zuhdi's basic experimental studies, was clinically used to prime and to replace blood loss from the field if needed on 38 patients by Nazih Zuhdi, Allen Greer and John Carey and eliminated special programs for blood recruitment at that time."

Soon afterward, Zuhdi, Carey, and Greer had already, following Zuhdi's hypothermic total intentional hemodilution experimental laboratory work, successfully operated on scores of patients using Zuhdi's Total Intentional Hemodilution with sugar solution to prime the heartlung machine, with his designed cell saver and with citrated banked blood to replace patient blood loss if needed. The first was clinically performed on February 25, 1960.

And then the history of Total Intentional Hemodilution, blood hematocrit and bloodless surgery sailed a new course in the world. Oklahoma was the port of origin.

# HISTORY OF TOTAL BODY PERFUSION

## The March to the Final Solution
## ala Nazih Zuhdi 1957-1960

"In the 1962-1963 and 1963-1964 editions of the *Yearbook of General Surgery*, Michael Debakey summarized approvingly another of Zuhdi and his colleagues' articles on "Total Intentional Hemodilution" and his commentary added, "We have been most impressed by ..."
"This article is significant ..."
And added in another commentary, "Many physiologic studies related to cardiopulmonary bypass with pooled homologous blood will require reevaluation ...."

ZUHDI'S INTENSE STEPS IN OKLAHOMA
• NORMOTHERMIC TOTAL BODY PERFUSION FOR OPEN HEART SURGERY,
1957-1958+ EXPERIMENTAL LABORATORY
• NORMOTHERMIC TOTAL BODY PERFUSION FOR OPEN HEART SURGERY,
1958-1959** EXPERIMENTAL LABORATORY
CLINICAL 1959* , 58 patients
• HYPOTHERMIC TOTAL BODY PERFUSION FOR OPEN HEART SURGERY,
1959** EXPERIMENTAL LABORATORY
CLINICAL 1959*, 43 patients
• CITRATED BANKED BLOOD FOR TOTAL BODY PERFUSION FOR OPEN HEART SURGERY,
1959 ** EXPERIMENTAL LABORATORY
CLINICAL 1959*, 38 patients
• ZUHDI'S TOTAL INTENTIONAL HEMODILUTION FOR OPEN-HEART SURGERY FOR ALL,
1959-1960** EXPERIMENTAL LABORATORY
CLINICAL February 25, 1960* first
AND OPENED THE GATES TO THE WHOLE WORLD

+Oklahoma University Medical College-Experimental Laboratory
*13th Street Mercy Hospital, Oklahoma City.
**Oklahoma City's 13th Street Mercy Hospital Heart and Research Institute - Experimental Laboratory.
Zuhdi, N., McCollough, B., Carey, J., and Greer, A.: The use of citrated bank blood for open-heart surgery. Anesthesiology, 21: 496-501, October, 1960 (description of total intentional hemodilution).

## Clarence Dennis

Clarence Dennis performed the first open heart surgery in the world in April 1951. It opened the gates for the new discipline of open heart surgery even though it was not successful.

Dennis also demonstrated the "salvage for the first time in the world" on November 1, 1954 of a long-term survivor of massive myocardial infarction and shock by temporary support with the pump oxygenator, to which Dennis acknowledged Zuhdi's specific contributions, as a mechanical assisted circulation device.

**THIS IS THE FORERUNNER TO ALL ARTIFICIAL BYPASS HEARTS, INCLUDING THE EXPERIMENTAL ZUHDI-RITCHIE BYPASS HEART OF 1963-1964—AT PRESENT THE PROPERTY OF THE OKLAHOMA HISTORY MUSEUM, AN AFFILIATE OF THE SMITHSONIAN INSTITUTION, AND ON PERMANENT EXHIBIT.**

Dennis performed his first successful open heart surgery with this same heart-lung machine on June 30, 1955, Zuhdi was present. Zuhdi was overwhelmed with the realization that, with Dennis, the medical landscape of the world had been changed forever.

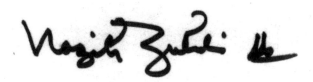

**Dr. Clarence Dennis. The inscription reads:**
"To my good friend and former co-worker Nazih Zuhdi
With Best Regards and Good Wishes, Clarence Dennis 3-21-70"

## CLARENCE DENNIS, M.D.
2332 Field Stone Drive
Mendota Heights, MN 55120

August 12, 1991

John Ross, Jr., M.D., F.A.C.C.
Chairman, Awards Committee
American College of Cardiology
Heart House
9111 Old Georgetown Road
Bethesda, MD 20814-1699

Dear Dr. Ross,

On return from a week's vacation in the norath woods, I found last evening a letter from Dr. D. K. C. Cooper of the Oklahoma Transplantation Institute suggesting that I might write you in support of his nomination of Nazih Zuhdi for a Distinguished Scientist Award by the American College of Cardiology. Today being the due date for receipt of such a letter by you, I am hastily writing this letter and sending it by Express Mail in the hope that this delay will be forgiven under the circustance of my having been out of reach during the interval.

I am delighted to support the proposal of this honor for Nazih Zuhdi and subscribe wholeheartedly to that proposal. Nazih served his residency with me and my associates at Downstate, completing same in 1956. He later had his training in Thoracic Surgery with Walt Lillehei, the seconder of this proposal, at the University of Minnesota.

During his training at Brooklyn, Zuhdi was a very bright star among the 50-odd residents in training there, always ready with suggestions and the drive to carry them through, which he did regularly in the year he worked with me in the research laboratory during our work on developing a pump-oxygenator, as a result of which we were able to salvage the first long-term survivor of massive myocardial infarction and shock by temporary circulatory support with that same pump-oxygenator.

His later work with use of banked blood as a prime for extracorporeal circulation was a major breakthrough, and his introduction of a blood-free prime, using dextrose solution, was a magnificent contribution. Zuhdi has provided many additional contributions to the field of cardiac surgery and to the field of transplantation, but in my opinion those just mentioned more than justify the proposed Award.

Zuhdi has remained a very good and highly regarded friend and is a true gentleman.

At this late stage in your selection procedure, I will not delay with more detail. I wish only to express my whoehearted approval of the proposed nomination.

If I may provide any additional information, please let me hear from you.

Respectfully yours,

Clarence Dennis, M.D., Ph.D., D.Sc.

# "THOSE WERE THE DAYS"—BEFORE THE YEAR 2000

## Dr. Clarence Dennis

"What were the benefits which come to me from all this effort,
aside from the information and the devices? They were many, but
mostly young people I have had the opportunity to watch learn
and contribute ... persons such as Nazih Zuhdi ... who worked with
us during his training and who later conceived and introduced the
technique of hemodilution in open heart work ..."

*Clarence Dennis*

DR. CLARENCE DENNIS, 1985 LAUREATE ADDRESS
AMERICAN SOCIETY OF ARTIFICIAL INTERNAL ORGANS

To Nazih — "Former Student, Master Surgeon, and a Very Special Friend! With My Admiration"
C. Walton Lillehei M.D. 9-10-83

Dr. C. Walton Lillehei, circa 1983

## "THOSE WERE THE DAYS"—BEFORE THE YEAR 2000

"I should also like to take the opportunity to do something I have been intending to do and that is to tell you how much I have admired your improvements in perfusion technique. As you know, if anything we were a little skeptical until Dick DeWall was down and visited you and he came back fully sold on it. I certainly consider it one of the most important advances in perfusion techniques. As you doubtless know from Dick, we have been advocating this enthusiastically to all who have visited here at the clinic and thus I am sure that others will come to appreciate its values."

DR. C. WALTON LILLEHEI,
PROFESSOR OF SURGERY,
UNIVERSITY OF MINNESOTA
LETTER TO DR. NAZIH ZUHDI, JULY 21, 1961

A statement of **Dr. C. Walton Lillehei during Dr. Nazih Zuhdi's induction into the Oklahoma Hall of Fame in November 1994:**

"Dr. Zuhdi, in the late 1950s, was the originator, creator, and inventor of hemodilution and the non-blood prime of the pump oxygenator for open heart surgery ... These days 2,000 [such] operations are done every 24 hours, 7 days a week worldwide. It is a safe and accurate assumption that not a single one is done without hemodilution. It's ironic that the history of the technique that is so effective and so universally used has been largely lost upon the recent generation of surgeons and cardiologists, not to mention our patients."

*Walton*

DR. C. WALTON LILLEHEI,
PROFESSOR OF SURGERY EMERITUS
UNIVERSITY OF MINNESOTA, 1995

C. WALTON LILLEHEI, PH.D., M.D.
73 OTIS LANE - ST. PAUL, MINNESOTA 55104

(612) 644-8660

August 2, 1991

John Ross, Jr., M.D.
Chairman, Awards Committee
American College of Cardiology
The Heart House
9111 Old Georgetown Road
Bethesda, MD 20814

RE: Nazih Zuhdi, M.D.
Director, Surgeon - in - Chief
Oklahoma Transplant Institute
Baptist Medical Center
Oklahoma City, OK 73112

Dear Dr. Ross:

I enthusiastically second the nomination of Dr. Zuhdi for the <u>Distinguished Scientist Award</u> of the College.

Dr. Zuhdi, in the late 1950's, was the originator, creator, inventor of the concept of hemodilution and the non-blood prime of the pump oxygenator for open heart surgery.

This development alone had an immediate explosive effect on the applicability of open heart surgery worldwide. Before Dr. Zuhdi's work, cardiac surgeons insisted on having fresh blood drawn into heparin from six to twelve or more donors, twelve hours or less before surgery. Obviously, this created a very great logistical problem, but was thought absolutely necessary. After Dr. Zuhdi's work, open heart surgery could be scheduled like any other major operation with only the cross-matching of a few units of banked blood necessary.

I first became acquainted with Dr. Zuhdi 35 years ago on July 1, 1956 when he began a six month training period on my cardiovascular service at the University of Minnesota. Dr. Zuhdi had already completed a period of six years of training in general and thoracic surgery in New York City. First, he had had a surgical internship at Columbia- Presbyterian University (George Humphreys, Chief), and five years in general and thoracic training at the Downstate University of New York (Dr. Clarence Dennis, Chief).

In looking thru Dr. Zuhdi's file for this letter, I find an internal memo from me dated September 1, 1956 to Dr. Wangensteen (then Chairman of the Department) describing Dr. Zuhdi as "brilliant" (after only two months with us). As time and events have evolved this proved to be a very prescient observation.

Following the completion of his training at Minnesota he went to the University of Oklahoma where he established a research laboratory along with his clinical duties. Very soon thereafter, he described a very significant and very important improvement of the already very simple disposable DeWall Lillehei bubble oxygenator. This refinement, which we immediately adopted, consisted of a stainless steel tube bent in the configuration of a helix and inserted within the plastic tubing of the helix reservoir of the oxygenator. Through the lumen of this stainless steel tube, hot or cold water would be readily circulated and provided an excellent heat exchanger, and at the same time reduced the already small priming volume necessary for this pump oxygenator.

Then, with this apparatus he took a giant step forward by showing in a series of animal studies that open heart perfusions without any blood prime were not only possible but very feasible for performance of open heart surgery. Moreover, the actual perfusions utilizing hemodilution by 5% glucose in water were physiologically, by all measurements, superior and postoperative blood loss was lessened. He found that the hemodilution, by lowering viscosity, greatly improved blood flow through the body and the absence of large quantities of foreign blood permitted normal blood clotting postoperatively. He immediately applied these findings to a series of patients, performing all types of open heart procedures with dramatically reduced blood requirements and clearly better perfusions. The benefits were unmistakable, and the rest was history!

These days, worldwide 2,000 open heart operations are done every 24 hours seven days a week. It is a safe and accurate assumption that not a single one of these operations was done without hemodilution. Thus, it's ironic that this technique is so effective and so universally used that the history of how it came about has been largely lost upon the present generation of surgeons and cardiologists, not to mention our patients.

The recognition of Dr. Zuhdi's momentous discovery that has had such a beneficial influence upon open heart surgery, itself one of the major medical developments of the 20th century, will be very well received by all. Moreover, the excellence of this choice will reflect favorably upon our College!

Sincerely yours,

C. Walton Lillehei, Ph.D., M.D.
Clinical Professor of Surgery
University of Minnesota Medical School,
Past President of the American College of Cardiology

CWL/pl

*The following letter was scanned in its entirety.*

RICHARD A. DeWALL, M.D.
421 THORNHILL ROAD
DAYTON, OHIO 45419

AUG 20

July 28, 1991

D.K.C. Cooper, M. D.
Oklahoma Transplantation Institute
Baptist Medical Center
3300 Northwest Expressway
Oklahoma City, Oklahoma  73112-44481

Dear Dr. Cooper:

It is with pleasure that I have the opportunity to support the nomination of Dr. Nazih Zuhdi for the American College of Cardiology, Distinguished Scientist award. Dr Zuhdi significantly advanced the practice of cardiopulmonary bypass with his introduction of the use of bank blood as an oxygenator prime, greatly easing the load on blood banks working with open heart surgical teams. This permitted the expansion of open heart surgery to many more patients at a lessor cost.

Following this Dr. Zuhdi introduced the use of 5% dextrose in water as an oxygenator prime with intentional hemo-dilution. This again expanded the applicability of open heart surgical techniques.

And open heart surgery was again advanced by Dr. Zuhdi's introduction and application of a controlled hypothermia technique for use during open heart surgery, which has been generally applied since that time.

Dr. Zuhdi has been a leader in open heart surgery and bypass techniques for several decades since the beginning of bypass supported surgery. Dr Zuhdi would be a most worthy recipient of the Distinguished Scientist award from the American College of Cardiolgy.

Sincerely,

*Richard DeWall*

Richard DeWall, M. D., F.R.C.S.

Open heart surgery in a private hospital was unheard of, and that was the beginning of the avalanche of open-heart surgery in every nook and cranny of the world. What university centers considered to be their own property, Zuhdi broke the barrier in 1960 and delivered it to all.

Among the earliest supporters was Dr. Herbert Warden at the University of West Virginia, who wrote Zuhdi on June 2, 1961,

"I have great admiration for what you have accomplished since going to Oklahoma, and this you have done under somewhat difficult circumstances which further adds to the credit due you."

# "THOSE WERE THE DAYS"—BEFORE THE YEAR 2000

Dr. Christiaan Barnard and Dr. Nazih Zuhdi were two trainees (July 1-December 30, 1956) in the heart program of Dr. C. Walton Lillehei at the University of Minnesota—later Chris went to South Africa and Nazih stayed in the U.S.

The world's first human-to-human heart transplant was accomplished December 3, 1967 by Christiaan Barnard, Capetown, South Africa. He described employeing: "...the heart lung machine...using the Hemodilution technique developed by my longtime friend and present colleague Nazih Zuhdi..."

CHRISTIAAN BARNARD
AS TOLD TO DAVID K.C. COOPER, M.D., Ph.D.
Professor of Surgery, University of Pittsburgh
*Health Signs*, December 4, 1987

*The following letter was scanned in its entirety.*

**Denton A. Cooley, M. D.**
**Texas Heart Institute**
**In The Texas Medical Center**
**Houston, Texas 77030**

August 18, 1999

Nazih Zuhdi, M.D.
Oklahoma Transplantation Institute
Integris Baptist Medical Center
3300 Northwest Expressway
Oklahoma City, OK 73112

Dear Nazih:

As you approach retirement from clinical practice I join your many admirers, grateful students and patients, and friends in wishing you good health and happiness.

Your career in surgery has truly been outstanding with many "firsts" in cardiovascular surgery. Of all those I believe your early investigations of blood substitutes in cardiopulmonary bypass was the most useful and practical. Your courage to apply this principle in clinical surgery made open heart surgery safer and available to large numbers of patients. Although skeptics of this departure from standard practice were vocal and often emotional, you persisted and convinced the entire surgical profession of the validity of this technique.

Throughout your impressive career you have followed a fearless path to further progress. The development of organ transplantation at your Institute is testimony to your eagerness to achieve.

From my earliest acquaintance with you in the era of exploration of the cardiac chambers, I have enjoyed your inspiring approach to innovations. Also, I have enjoyed your friendship and hospitable spirit.

Good luck in the years ahead.

Sincerely yours,

Denton A. Cooley, M.D.

DAC:jm

## "THOSE WERE THE DAYS"—BEFORE THE YEAR 2000

Three giants for their remarkable contributions in open-heart surgery merit my gratitude:

**Michael DeBakey (1908-2008)** said that Zuhdi's Total Intentional Hemodilution is "impressive," and added, in another commentary, "Many physiologic studies related to cardiopulmonary bypass with pooled homologous blood will require re-evaluation..."

**Denton Cooley (1920- )** described Zuhdi's work as a "major breakthrough."

**Herbert Warden (1920-2002)** stated to Zuhdi that the history of open-heart surgery with a heart-lung machine is best described as "pre-Zuhdi and post-Zuhdi."

# MAPPING THE REACH OF TOTAL INTENTIONAL HEMODILUTION

In the early years, Zuhdi kept a five-by-three-foot map of the world on his office wall. As news of another doctor or institution using total intentional hemodilution came to him whether by media or personal contact, Zuhdi put another pin in the map on the wall. In this way, he kept track of the spread of the principle of total intentional hemodilution. It started slowly — two or three centers in 1960, around a dozen in 1961 — but by 1965, the map had become so covered with pins that its effectiveness as a marker came to an end. The pin-encrusted map was evidence that, outside of some dormant universities still in Rip Van Winkle's somnolence, total intentional hemodilution was no longer news; it had become common practice. Even the University of Oklahoma had yielded to the inevitable and quietly without fanfare adopted it. The path of heart surgeons everywhere had moved through Mercy Hospital and Oklahoma City and out to the entire world. A representative letter to Zuhdi on June 19, 1962 from R. D. Sautter of the Marshfield Clinic, Marshfield, Wisconsin, illustrates the course of the stampede: "You can now place another pin on your map in your office, for last week I successfully completed my first open-heart surgery. The run was smooth as silk."

*Richard Green, profiling Allen Greer for the* Oklahoma State Journal of Medicine *in March of 1996, stated that Greer "does credit Zuhdi with the idea and the research for the group's single most important innovation, hemodilution. Priming the heart-lung machine with sugar water almost eliminated the need for cross-matched blood and turned out to be beneficial to the surgical patient." That breakthrough occurred experimentally in 1959 and clinically on February 25, 1960. It was the first in the world and it was successful.*

## "THOSE WERE THE DAYS"—BEFORE THE YEAR 2000

Noted researcher and medical historian Dr. Richard J. Bing of the University of Southern California addressed a surprising implication decades later that surfaced in a book of which he was editor, writing Zuhdi on September 5, 2003

"As I wrote you, I deeply regret any errors that have clouded the particular chapter in the book. I regret this particularly since I have tremendous admiration for your work that as Dr. Lillehei has stated, was a tremendous discovery. I assure you that our mutual feelings for each other as well as my respect for you remain high."

RICHARD J. BING, M.D.
PROFESSOR OF MEDICINE, USC (Em),
DIRECTOR OF EXPERIMENTAL CARDIOLOGY,
HUNTINGTON MEDICAL RESEARCH INSTITUTE,
VISITING ASSOCIATE IN CHEMISTRY, CALIFORNIA
INSTITUTE OF TECHNOLOGY

I have heard and seen with wonder so many renditions and variations of what came about in our remarkable institutions in New York, in Minneapolis and in Oklahoma.

I witnessed endless shenanigans, best described with the words of Albert Einstein he used for another matter, "primitive and pretty childish."

To continue climbing new mountains to new heights, I borrow the words of Brooks Barr:

"What we owe to our past and our future is the truth. Not rumors, not hearsay, not embellishments, not presumptions, not distortions, simply the honor of the truth."

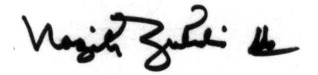

Our past is all the heritage we have — the foundation for our todays and signpost to our tomorrows. Our future depends on the integrity of that knowledge. The safekeeping of its truth is twofold. First, those who create history must record it accurately. Second, those who pass it to succeeding generations must verify and report it honestly and clearly. Can a poisoned well ever be clean again?

Yousef Khanfar

Yousef Khanfar

## "WHY DID I WANT THESE FACTUAL RENDITIONS TO BE WRITTEN? IT IS BECAUSE OF A COMPULSION TO CORRECT THE TARNISHED IMAGE OF MEDICINE."

### So did Dwight Harken express his thoughts. I agree.

**C. Walton Lillehei, "King of Hearts," University of Minnesota, Minneapolis, Minn., wrote Nazih Zuhdi on July 21, 1961:**
"I should also like to take the opportunity to do something I have been intending to do and that is tell you how much I have admired your improvements in perfusion technique. As you know, if anything we were a little skeptical until Dick DeWall was down and visited you and he came back fully sold on it. I certainly consider it one of the most important advances in perfusion techniques. As you doubtless know from Dick, we have been advocating this enthusiastically to all whom have visited here at the clinic and thus I am sure that others will come to appreciate its values."

**Dr. Tetsuzo Akutsu, a leading heart surgeon and researcher in Japan, wrote to Zuhdi when he was a research associate at the Cleveland Clinic, Ohio, on July 5, 1961:**
" ... Since Dr. W.J. Kolff came back from a visit to your hospital in May, we have done five perfusion experiments with your technique ... We intend to use this technique in total replacement of the natural heart with an artificial heart inside the chest, one experiment being done last week with success. I would appreciate it very much if you could send me all your papers ... Thank you very much for your consideration."

**Dr. Albert Starr of the Starr-Edwards Valvular Prosthesis at the University of Oregon Medical School, Portland, Oregon, wrote to Zuhdi on October 3, 1962:**
" ... We are most impressed with your excellent work ... and I know that Dr. Vettath would profit greatly from talking with you and seeing your team in action."

Robert G. Richardson, writing in *The Scalpel and the Heart*, published in 1970, outlined the origin of hemodilution succinctly:

"Nazih Zuhdi and his colleagues at Oklahoma City settled for 5 percent dextrose in distilled water with a moderate degree of internal hypothermia (to cut down the oxygen requirements and so compensate for the dilution of the blood); other surgeons followed suit with considerable success. Denton Cooley of Houston, Texas, picked up the idea from Zuhdi's early reports in 1960 ..."

In a letter to Clarence Dennis, May 8, 1963, Zuhdi gave a partial but indicative list of some of the surgeons who came to Mercy Hospital in 1960 and early 1961, who signed the guest book. Sister Mary Alvera later gave it to Zuhdi as a capsule of these momentous times. The roster included: Dr. P. Lavadia, Phillippines; Dr. T.E. Ashley and Dr. T. Cochrane, Springfield, Missouri; Dr. M. Chamberlain, Dr. B. Potter and Dr. T. McNeill, New York City; Dr. W. Kolff, Cleveland, Ohio; Dr. Malm, Sweden; Dr. J. Gonzalez, Mexico City; Dr. N.S. Ahlowalia, India; Dr. R. Holliday, New York; Dr. Huff, California; Dr. Kerban, Lebanon; Dr. V.R. Kimel, New Jersey; Dr. Merikitani, Honolulu, Hawaii; and Dr. E. Guertzenstein, Rio de Janerio, Brazil.

Clarence Dennis performed the world's first open-heart surgery with a heart-lung machine of his design in April, 1951 at the University of Minnesota, Minneapolis, Minnesota. It was not successful. Nazih Zuhdi joined his residency program at the State University of New York - Downstate Medical Center, the new domain of Dennis, in July, 1952. Dennis wrote his former student on June 29, 1963:

"Your place in American medicine will be sure and the esteem in which you are held will be greater, in my opinion, if you ignore such petty moves as those which have so disturbed you."

About thirteen years later, Zuhdi's dear friend and co-resident at the C. Walton Lillehei Heart Service during the second half of 1956, the late Christiaan Barnard, performed the world's first heart transplant in Cape Town, South Africa, in December, 1967—using Nazih Zuhdi's hypothermic Total Intentional Hemodilution.

Nazih Zuhdi studied total body perfusion as a research trainee with Professor Clarence Dennis in 1952 and Professor C. Walton Lillehei in 1956, and as an independent researcher through the University of Oklahoma Medical College in 1957 and through Mercy Hospital Heart and Research Institute in 1958-1965.

It was in 1959 that Nazih Zuhdi declared, " ... the entire perfusion system emerged to me as lucid as the alphabet. Having cleared the past waves of the ocean, a true, uncluttered vision occurred. I absorbed myself in my research and kept going in my experimental laboratory at Mercy Hospital Heart and Research Institute. I realized then what I was doing was correct. It turned out to be the gateway to varied disciplines for the benefit of mankind."

Nazih Zuhdi in an interview to Jane Fried, *Public Medical News*, 1989:

> That vision, the concept of total intentional hemodilution —
> the replacement of the blood in the heart-lung machine with
> a non-blood prime producing dilution of blood — divided
> open-heart surgery into two eras, said Herbert Warden of
> the University of West Virginia: The pre-Zuhdi era and the
> post- Zuhdi era. Its revelation was not a sudden apparition,
> not a quick fix for a crisis, nor an expedient response to the
> pleas of any group. Its clarity coalesced in the cauldron
> of the many years of Zuhdi's experience and dedicated
> efforts and research. Its incisiveness overturned decades
> of accepted scientific thinking, as entrenched tradition had
> taught doctors and surgeons to minimize any intrusion on the
> "milieu interieur" of the human body.

"To dilute the blood to such an extent in a human being …was against all our conditioned reflexes as physicians. Of course, I am very gratified that you did so successfully."

—Frank Gollan, in a letter to Nazih Zuhdi, December 26, 1960.

Total Intentional Hemodilution opened the door to new possibilities that stretched the limits to what we thought had been possible in dealing with the physical body. The process pointed the way to new frontiers of healing. It democratized the concept of hematocrit. The product of a vision bred of research, Nazih Zuhdi disseminated its benefits for all: all races, all religions, all cultures, in all parts of the globe.

"I have great admiration for what you have accomplished since going to Oklahoma, and this you have done under somewhat difficult circumstances which further add to the credit due you."

—Dr. Herbert Warden, Professor of Surgery and Chairman of the Surgery Department at the University of West Virginia, in a letter to Nazih Zuhdi, June 2, 1962

"Dr. Zuhdi, in the late 1950s, was the originator, creator, and inventor of hemodilution and the non-blood prime of the pump oxgenator for open heart surgery … It's ironic that the history of the technique that is so effective and so universally used has been largely lost upon the recent generation of surgeons and cardiologists, not to mention our patients."

Dr. C. Walton Lillehei,
Professor of Surgery Emeritus
University of Minnesota, 1995

## AND...IN 1960

**Ginger Litsey's mission in life was to save babies around the world.**

# A NEW VOYAGE EMBARKS FROM OKLAHOMA TO THE WORLD

### Saving Mothers and As Yet Unborn Babies

**February 25, 1960**

And then the history of Zuhdi's Total Intentional Hemodilution sailed a new course in the world. Oklahoma, through Nazih Zuhdi, Allen Greer and John Carey, founded 13th Street Mercy Hospital Heart and Research Institute and its Zuhdi-chaired experimental laboratory. It was again the point of origin for the next bold new voyage.

**March 31, 1960**

Elizabeth Litsey believed in life. She, however, was faced with a terrible choice. She needed open heart surgery. But it was, at that time, an absolute contraindication to perform such surgery on a pregnant woman. Lose her baby or lose her life, if not both.

GINGER LITSEY, above, with her mother Elizabeth; and, at left, as a young, beautiful, and vivacious woman.

  That judgment was not good enough for her. Nor was it good enough because of the experimental, beneficial effects of Total Intentional Hemodilution in the microcirculation that Zuhdi observed in his experimental laboratory at Mercy Hospital Heart and Research Institute. Barely over a month after the epochal first surgery on Terry Gene Nix, on February 25, 1960, using Zuhdi's Total Intentional Hemodilution, Nazih Zuhdi and John Carey (Allen Greer was away) steered successfully into that forbidden port, opening up whole new possibilities for life. Both mother and baby survived and thrived. Ginger Litsey grew to a beautiful young lady. Unfortunately she was killed in an automobile accident 38 years later, but that was not the end of her testament to life.

  Elizabeth Litsey died only recently. Her niece Amber worked at the Nazih Zuhdi Transplant Institute at Integris Baptist Medical Center for many years, the living image of the miracle first dared in Oklahoma City at 13th Street Mercy Hospital. And can one count the number of babies born out of the medical harbor first opened in landbound Oklahoma?

AND...IN 1963

## ZUHDI-RITCHIE
## ARTIFICIAL VENTRICULAR
## BY-PASS HEART DEVICES

At present, the Zuhdi-Ritchie
Artificial Ventricular By-Pass Heart
Device that functioned in an
admirable fashion for four days in a
dog is the property of the Oklahoma
History Center, an affiliate of the
Smithsonian Institution at
Washington D.C.
It is also on permanent exhibit at
the Oklahoma History Center
800 Nazih Zuhdi Drive
Oklahoma City, Oklahoma 73105.

## "THOSE WERE THE DAYS"—BEFORE THE YEAR 2000

Dr. Tetsuzo Akutsu, a leading researcher, wrote to Dr. Nazih Zuhdi when he was a Research Associate at the Cleveland Clinic, Ohio, on July 5, 1961:

"I have been very much impressed and interested in your experimental and clinical works in open-heart surgery with the use of low flow hypothermic (hemodilution) perfusion.

Since Dr. W.J. Kolff came back from a visit to your hospital in May, we have done five perfusion experiments with your technique. Four of five dogs survived, and in two of them, venae cavae were occluded for 30 minutes, in the other for 60 minutes.

We intend to use this technique in total replacement of the natural heart with an artificial heart inside the chest, one experiment being done last week with success. I would appreciate it very much if you could send me all your papers ... Thank you very much for your consideration."

During that period of time, Zuhdi was using his total intentional hemodilution for his own animal experimental artificial bypass hearts. From 1988 onward, his transplant institute would be using total intentional hemodilution for all human artificial bypass heart surgeries and total heart replacements.

Yousef Khanfar

*This letter was scanned in its entirety.*

CLEVELAND CLINIC     **ATTACHMENT 4**
2020 EAST 93RD STREET
CLEVELAND 6, OHIO

DEPARTMENT OF ARTIFICIAL ORGANS
WILLEM J. KOLFF, M.D.

10/26/61

October 23, 1961

Nazih Zuhdi, M.D.
Lister Medical Building
430 N.W. 12th Street
Oklahoma City3, Oklahoma

Dear Dr. Zuhdi:

It would be greatly appreciated if you would send a collection of your reprints concerning the helix reservoir bubble
oxygenator to Dr. Knud Palle Taarnhoj at the Copenhagen County
Hospital in Glostrup, Denmark.

Sincerely yours,

Willem J. Kolff, M.D.

*Do not send to many
make a selection of important ones.
Hope this finds you well.*

## DEVICE TO BE READY IN FIVE YEARS, SURGEON SAYS

# Plastic Hearts To Assist Weakened Ones

**BY HARRY NELSON**

Implanted plastic hearts that take the load off of failing hearts will be practical within five years, an Oklahoma surgeon said here Tuesday.

"Our goal is to make hearts unbreakable, hearts that will last forever," said Dr. Nazih Zuhdi, chairman of the research committee of Mercy Hospital in Oklahoma City.

He has already succeeded in keeping a dog alive 96 hours with an implanted device to assist circulation powered by a tiny pump strapped to the animal's back.

It would be possible, the surgeon said, to do the same for a human patient but the present equipment would extend the patient's life only a few days. The minimum he would accept for a working model for human use would be one that would work at least three years. This he said in an interview at the Ambassador, where he addressed a meeting of the American College of Chest Physicians will be possible within five years. Dr. Alfred Goldman, chief of thoracic surgery at Cedars-Sinai Medical Center is chairman of the meeting.

The goal of the research ultimately is to perfect a device that can be installed in heart attack prone persons before they have an attack so that the artificial heart could take over the pumping action of the stricken heart and save the patient's life.

While at least three other research teams also are engaged in a race to develop a practical artificial heart, Dr. Zuhdi's model differs in several respects.

The goal of several is to perfect models that totally replace the patient's own heart.

Dr. Zuhdi feels there is no need to replace the whole heart but merely to substitute for that percentage of pumping action that the patient's own heart lacks. His artificial model consists of a plastic bulb about three inches in diameter with an inner sphere. Two plastic tubes with valves extend from either side of the bulb. One tube is sewn into a heart chamber and the other into the aorta, the artery that carries blood from the heart.

A portable pump that weighs 3-pounds is outside the body. Implanted and working, the net effect is for the device to help the patient's damaged heart to pump enough blood to keep him alive. One reason for concentrating on a partial heart rather than a total one is the difficult-to-solve problem of supplying enough power to keep the device working for long periods, the surgeon said. While only one watt is needed to move one liter of blood, because of resistance and other problems the actual power requirement is 48 watts. Because at least five liters must be pumped every minute, the energy source must be far greater than is now practical.

Requiring that the pump only assist rather than do the full job of circulating will considerably reduce the energy requirements, according to the surgeon.

Other teams engaged in similar work are headed by Dr. Michael E. DeBakey of Baylor University, Houston, and Dr. Adrian Kantrowitz of Maimonides Hospital, Brooklyn.

Dr. DeBakey installed an assist-heart similar to Dr. Zuhdi's in a patient more than two years ago. The patient lived four days. He said several weeks ago he will be ready to do another soon.

Another speaker, Dr. Phillip Callahan, assistant chief of surgery at Denver General Hospital, described another method of helping ailing hearts. Rather than using an implanted artificial heart, the surgeon and a team of engineers have developed a special pump that reduces the workload of the heart.

The pump is attached by a plastic tube inserted into a leg artery. It forces blood into the circulation in pulsations that are timed to coincide with the heart's natural pulse pressure.

According to Dr. Callahan, the pump can do up to 40% of the heart's workload and can continue this for an indefinite period. The patient, of course, is confined to bed.

Dr. Callahan said that in addition to heart attacks, the pump has been used to save persons with massive hemorrhage and to assist the circulation of patients with a weak heart who must undergo major surgery.

# THE ARTIFICIAL BYPASS HEART
## 1954, to 1963-1965, to 1988, to 1996 and Forward to 2010 and Beyond

*Clarence Dennis also demonstrated the "salvage for the first time in the world on **November 1, 1954** (Zuhdi was a 'co-worker' and co-author in the associated article) long-term survivor of massive myocardial infarction and shock by temporary support with his pump oxygenator as stated in his letter."*

*In order to continue, Nazih Zuhdi's vision of a center to have a full scale artificial heart program, he had to bring into existence a total infrastructure that is different from all experimental and clinical available services at Nazih Zuhdi Transplant Institute and INTEGRIS.*

*A revelation from God, through Dr. Zuhdi's scientist-in-residence Dr. David Cooper, led Dr. David Nelson to become a distinctive member of Zuhdi's team in 1994. After all, he had worked with Dr. James Long, starting in 1992, and James Long was Dr. Zuhdi's choice to head the program. James Long was a 1989 graduate of the longest standing experimental laboratory founded by W.J. Kolff—it produced the most well-known artificial heart scientist-surgeons. The circle of remarkable achievements of Dr. W. J. Kolff, who visited Dr. Zuhdi in **1961** had been fulfilled when Dr. James Long became the seamless transition for Dr. Zuhdi—initiated in 1994.*

Recently Dr. Nazih Zuhdi reviewed the minutes of a 1965 meeting in which he updated some of the artificial bypass heart prototypes that led to the groundbreaking for his artificial bypass heart he developed with Lieutenant Navy Commander Clark Ritchie at Mercy Hospital Heart and Research Institute— Experimental Laboraotry chaired by Zuhdi. Zuhdi revisualized the series of experiments of almost half a century before, but with a tinge of sadness. He himself had lived to survive the shenanigans of life, but those innovative fruits of his labor on the heart-lung machine, the total body perfusion, Total Intentional Hemodilution and the artificial bypass hearts— except one had vanished into the trash of Baptist Hospital, discarded in the year 2000 on the whim of a cleaning crew and a vice president. Gone now, they were the products of his mind and heart—Gone. But the memory remains and it is quietly mourned.

The one artificial bypass heart that survived was kept all of these years by Annette McMichael, a nursing student who, with nursing student Violet McAuliff, helped Zuhdi place that particular artificial bypass heart into a dog who survived for 96 hours—a feat at that time. This artificial bypass heart is now on permanent exhibit and the property of the Oklahoma History Center, an affiliate of the Smithsonian Institution. That moment in **1963** started the romance in which later the student, Nurse Annette McMichael, became Annette Zuhdi.

Twenty-five years later in **1988**, Nazih Zuhdi, Dimitri Novitzky, and David Cooper implanted a left ventricular assist device and a right ventricular assist device of Thoratec type that functioned well for four months until a heart became available for a successful transplant.

Since **1996**, with Dr. David Nelson as the facilitator, and as of **July 2011**, under the umbrella of Dr. James Long, **198** left verticular assist device (LVADS) implantations had been performed on NZTI patients either at Latter Day Saints Hospital in Salt Lake City, Utah (41 patients), or at INTEGRIS Nazih Zuhdi Transplantation Institute (157 patients). Zuhdi, at 88 years of his life and feeling the warm breezes of the skies, is satisfied and secure that James Long will continue Nazih Zuhdi Transplant Institute legacy of climbing new mountains to their summits in research, innovation, discoveries and patient care.

Later in **2010**, Dr. James Long, a world-acknowledged authority on artificial hearts, has become the seamless transition as the head of **Nazih Zuhdi Transplantation Institute** and artificial heart section—both experimental and clinical. "I am a firm believer that Nazih Zuhdi Transplantation Institute will continue to be a world recognized and admired center for all modalities of artificial hearts— as a bridge for transplantation or as 'destination therapy'," Zuhdi says.

In **2010**, Long replaced in totality the failing hearts of **three** patients with artificial hearts, and one in **2011**.

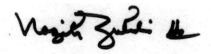

**Dates and figures were collected and verified by Dr. David P. Nelson.**

MINUTES OF THE RESEARCH COMMITTEE MEETING

| | |
|---|---|
| Date: | May 28, 1965 |
| Time: | 7:00 A.M. |
| Place: | House Staff Dining Room |
| Members Present: | Dr. Zuhdi, Chairman; Drs. Brown and Cutter |
| Also Present: | Hubert Jennings |

The meeting was called to order by the Chairman. The minutes of the previous meeting were not read due to lack of time.

**American Heart Association Grants:**   There was a brief discussion regarding the latest bulletin from the American Heart Association concerning research fellowships and grants-in-aid. Dr. Zuhdi said he would contact Dr. Carleton B. Chapman, President of the American Heart Association, whom he knew.

**NIH Grant:**   Dr. Zuhdi asked Dr. Cutter to furnish him with a curriculum vitae today as an effort will be made to complete application for the NIH grant this weekend.

**Research:**   Dr. Zuhdi reported that work in the research laboratory included eight left bypass implanted hearts. The longest survival was 96 hours. All the others lasted less than 15 hours except one which lasted about 24 hours. The problem has been mainly with the venous drainage and venous line. The design has been changed to conform with what has been learned from these experiments. This research is costly because as soon as an implanted heart is placed in a dog, it is already obsolete. Each change in design will cost $750.00 so if there are five changes, the expense will be close to $5,000. It is hoped that the money received from the State Health Department will be used for this research unless it is to be used for some other facets by the Administrator.

One implanted heart procedure has been performed each week. These procedures shall be continued until twelve have been completed.

**Publicity:**   It was Dr. Zuhdi's opinion that the work on the implanted heart should now be publicized, particularly in view of the new code of the County Medical Society which recognizes physicians as private citizens and privileged to mention their own research without qualms as do physicians engaged in research full time and physicians in other states. Dr. Cutter was not sure that this code had been adopted by the Society as a whole although it was out of committee. He agreed there should be some publicity now as he thought the survival of one experimental animal for 96 hours was miraculous. Also, Dr. Zuhdi is holding down two full-time jobs, one in research and one in private practice. He is not being compensated for his research work so, certainly, it could be ethically publicized.

Dr. Zuhdi felt the background, i.e., the start of the research, and all the different designs should be included in any publicity. He asked the group's opinion as to whether both the DAILY OKLAHOMAN and THE OKLAHOMA JOURNAL should be contacted. It was suggested that he request Mr. Roby's help in writing and publicizing the article.

Dr. Zuhdi recalled that THE CATHOLIC DIGEST published the team's article on "Hemodilution" at a time when such procedure was being highly criticized, and the article was quoted many times. He thought perhaps the Administrator might take care of publication of the article in "The Digest."

There being no further business to come before the Committee, the meeting adjourned at 7:30 A.M.

Nazih Zuhdi, M.D.
Chairman

**Minutes were kept for each meeting of the Research Comittee.**

Yousef Khanfar

# ZUHDI-RITCHIE RIGHT AND LEFT VENTRICULAR ASSIST DEVICES

## (1963-1965)

Photo of one of the experimental artificial bypass hearts from Zuhdi-Ritchie's work at the 13th Street Mercy Hospital Heart and Research Institute-Experimental Laboratory from 1963 to 1965.

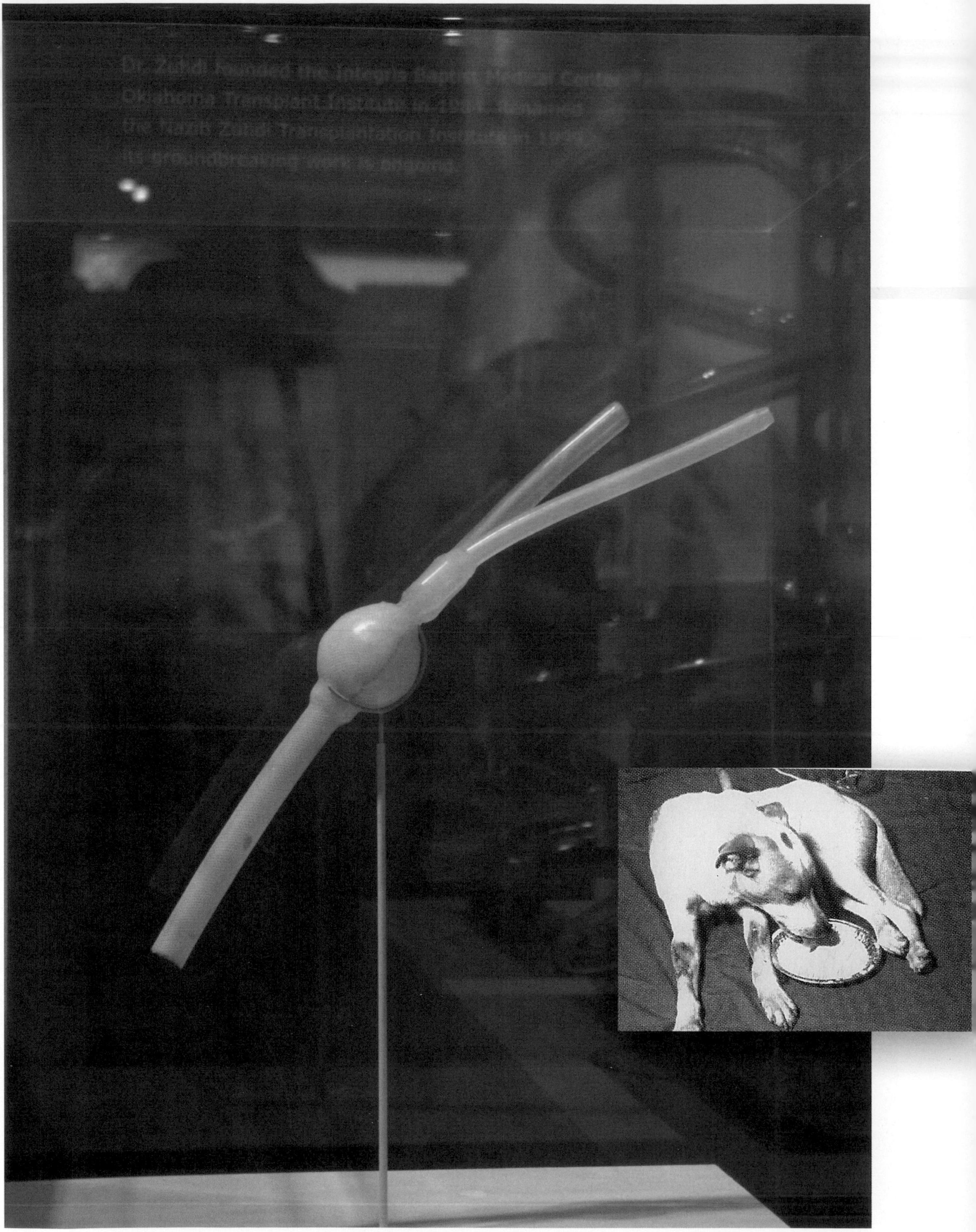

## ZUHDI-RITCHIE BYPASS HEART

### (1963 - 1964)

This artificial bypass heart (1963-1964), pictured on the opposite page, is the only one of its kind in the world. The 13th street Mercy Hospital Heart and Research Institute—Experimental Laboratory supported the work of Dr. Zuhdi and engineer Navy Lt. Commander Clark Ritchie (relocated to Oklahoma City by philanthropist John Kirkpatrick). Zuhdi and Ritchie collaborated closely in the development of artificial bypass hearts.

This bypass artificial heart is now the property of the Oklahoma History Center where it is preserved and on exhibit for future generations.

LEFT: Merci lived with the artificial bypass heart for four days. The Zuhdi-Ritchie Artificial Bypass Heart was saved by Zuhdi's wife, Annette, in a closet at home! She kept it as a souvenir because she had assisted him as a student nurse with the dog in the experimental laboratory.

PHOTOGRAPH BY JIM MEEKS, CURATOR OF THE OKLAHOMA HISTORY CENTER, 800 NAZIH ZUHDI DRIVE, OKLAHOMA CITY, OK

# A WORD FROM THE NZTI MEDICAL DIRECTOR

"It builds on the incredible history of pioneering and performance we have here, starting with the Nazih Zuhdi era that brought something to Oklahoma that might not have been here otherwise."

Dr. James Long, M.D., Ph.D.
Medical Director,
INTEGRIS Nazih Zuhdi
Transplantation Institute

Dr. Long was 3 years old in 1954 when Dr. Clarence Dennis used for the first time in the world a pump oxygenator, to which he acknowledges Zuhdi's contributions, as a mechanical assisted circulation device to a failing heart. It was successful.

## THE RELOCATION

**Nazih Zuhdi, Allen Greer and John Carey
From 13th Street Mercy Hospital,
Oklahoma City, Oklahoma (1958-1963)**

**To Baptist Medical Center
Oklahoma City, Oklahoma (1963-2010)**

**James Long is a promise to continue Nazih Zuhdi's legacy at
Integris and in Oklahoma, in the nation and in the world.**

Among the earliest supporters of Nazih Zuhdi was Dr. Herbert Warden at the University of West Virginia, who wrote Zuhdi on June 2, 1961: "I have great admiration for what you have accomplished since going to Oklahoma, and this you have done under somewhat difficult circumstances which further adds to the credit due you."

## STATE-OF-THE-ART INNOVATIVE ERA  1957-2010

## "THOSE WERE THE DAYS"—BEFORE THE YEAR 2000

According to Tyler Thomas of the Archives of the Sisters of Mercy, the first open-heart surgery in the state of Oklahoma was performed by Nazih Zuhdi, Allen Greer and John Carey at 13th Street Mercy Hospital on January 8, 1959—initiating a program of progressive experimental research and clinical applications that became a vibrant center, and setting a new course for open-heart surgery, total body perfusion, bloodless surgery and their derivatives in the state, in the nation, and in the world.

Then, with the relocation to Baptist Hospital, on April 1, 1963, Nazih Zuhdi and John Carey performed the first open-heart surgery at Baptist Hospital in Oklahoma City. This initiated for over 40 years a state-of-the-art innovative era with scientific publications, books and honors that placed Baptist Hospital on a unique platform. In addition, it was a reference center for scientists and physicians to come for education and to take our protocols around the world.

They are truly the beginning of today's Oklahoma Heart Hospital, Integris Heart Hospital and the Nazih Zuhdi Transplantation Institute— and, of course, adopted by the world.

At the end of the musical Camelot, Arthur knights a small boy, whom
he sends off with the famous instructions,
"Ask every person if he has heard the story
And tell it loud and clear if he has not
That there once was a fleeting wisp of glory called Camelot."
In the musical version of the Arthurian legend, Arthur says to
Pellinore that this is "what we all are–less than a drop in the
bright blue motion of the sunlit seas."
"But some of those drops," he says, "do sparkle ..."
Yes, some do sparkle.

In most significant human events, there is a web of people and circumstances, which interact to influence, and at time,
predict a signal event. This book contains the remembrances of
some such people: teachers, co-researchers, professional colleagues, enablers, skeptics, helpers, students and patients who
have had an influence on the career of Nazih Zuhdi, M.D.

# THE HOUSE THAT ZUHDI BUILT: THE PIONEERS 1950-2000

The task of taming a new land had been the work of a generation of pioneers and associates who had paved the road with Zuhdi. Their names should not be forgotten and are recorded here in grateful appreciation — Clarence Dennis, Charles Fries, Karl Karlson, Monty Duval, C. Walton Lillehei, Herbert Warden, Richard DeWall, Vincent Gott, William Weirich, Mathias Paneth, Aiman Hakim, John Schilling, John Kirkpatrick, E.K. Gaylord, John Nichols, Allen Greer, John Carey, Sam Musallam, Betty Blackburn, Nello Brown, Stout, Wiley McCollum, Modine Pierce, Terry G. Nix, Mary Fagella, Ida Bearhead, Ali Alli, Farouk Kanaa, Mary Spencer, Sister Mary Coletta, Sister Mary Alvera, Forest Lingenfelter, John Montroy, Karl Krieger, Richard Shifrin, John Kirkpatrick, Clark Ritchie, John Donnell, Galen Robbins, Vi Schlegel, Sue Lowe, Annette McMichael, Jerry Richards, Sally Burks, Bill Shawn, James Grim, Jack Gilleran, John Salmeron, Steve Rhodes, Ron Powell, John Muchmore, Sam Dahr, Kenneth Bonds, Jay Henry, James Hampton, Cheryl Montgomery, Faye May, Raul Chanes, Kenneth Potts, Leland and Vicki Gourley, Jane Fried, John Zweicker, Pat Sumpter, Cheryl Montgomery, Gerald Jenison, Vadakep Ramgopal, Dodge Hill, Riley Finley, Roberta Billy, Paul Lambert Bob Blackburn, Dan Provo, Doris Montoya, Dennis Parker, Christiaan Barnard, David Vanhooser, John Chaffin, Max Edgar, Scott Samara, David Cooper, Hartwell Dunn, Vivek Kohli, Bobbie Gene Smith, Paul Donat, Sandy Sanbar, Mark Sullivan, James P. Linn, Thomas Lynn, Stanley Hupfeld, Demitri Novitzky, Karen Allen, Sherrey Kesinger, Randy Cloud, Betty Litsey, Stanley Shrago, TheodoreViolett, Jerry Bressie, Marilyn Mash, Shelby Barnes, Marilyn Mash, Donna Jones, Jan Krebiel, Lura Futlon, Ellen Moran, Maria Schrader, Sherrie Kessinger, Lisa Daves, Linda Barger, Laura Fulton, Ellen Moran, Jan Locklear, Maria Schrader, Norman Imes, Irvin Paradis, Ye Yong, Louis Mieles, Hadar Merhav, Ghazi Rayan, Tommie Hewett, Jay Harolds, Georganne Snowden, Joe Cardello, Pam Reynolds, David Kraft, Sandy Savage, Sharon McCarty, Peggy Kraft, S.K. Bhatia, Bart Borsky, Karen Allen, Doretta Patrick, Roberta Billy, Lisa Daves, Linda Barger, Doris Montoya, Bradley Gaway, Basil Hassoun, Bakr Nour, Nathan Lidsky, Barbara Kerwin, David Van Thiel, Judith Gavaler, Harlan Wright, Ahmet Gurakar, Bev Barnes, Donna Jones, Jan Krebiel, Yi Huang, Shi-Feng Li, Dang Long, Roy Monlux, Eliezer Katz, Anthony Sebastian, Mel Clark, Mannie Villafana, Joan Imes, Rose Lane and Yousef Khanfar, David Nelson and James Long among them. Zuhdi was associated with them for their brilliant and unconventional thinking, because they went where others dared not go. Together this group of pioneers — educators, researchers, physicians, nurses, perfusionists, physician assistants, and technicians — put in place the structures of "The House That Zuhdi Built." Zuhdi had carved the town out of the wilderness. Zuhdi is confident James Long will continue the legacy.

*"Nazih Zuhdi,*
*The first time I equate humility with pride."*

**Cecilia Casas, RSM**

# BIBLIOGRAPHY

**SCIENTIFIC PUBLICATIONS.**
Lyons, H.A., Zuhdi, N., and Kydd D.M.:
The effects of carbonic anhydrase inhibitor on arterial blood gases in chronic pulmonary emphysema; a preliminary report. *American Journal of Medical Science* 229: 193-198, 1955. *Condensed in the series of Year Book of Medicine, 1955-1956.

Zuhdi, N. and Lyons, H.:
Angiocardiographic study of a case of double aortic arch without symptoms. *American Journal of Medicine* 28: 1022-1025, 1955.

Lyons, H., Zuhdi, N., and Kelly, J.:
Pectus excavatum. Funnel Breast, A cause of impaired ventricular distensibility as exhibited by right ventricular pressure pattern. *American Heart Journal* 50: 921-922, 1955.

Newman, M., Stuckey, J., Levowitz, B., Young, L., Dennis, C., Fries, C., Gorayeb, E., Zuhdi, N., Karlson, A., Adler, S., and Gliedman, M.:
Complete and partial perfusion of animal and human subjects with the pump oxygenator. *Year Book of Surgery* 38: 30-37, 1955.

Gott, V., Gonzales, J., Zuhdi, N., Varco, R., and Lillehei, C.W.:
Retrograde perfusion of the coronary sinus for direct vision aortic surgery. Surgery, Gynecology & Obstetrics 104: 319-328, 1957. *Condensed in series of *Year Book of Surgery,* editor Michael DeBakey, 1957.

Gott, V., DeWall, R., Paneth, M., Zuhdi, N., Weirich, W., Varco, R., and Lillehei, C.W.:
A self-contained disposable oxygenator of plastic sheet for intracardiac surgery. Thorax 12: 1-9, 1957. *Condensed in series of Y*ear Book of Surgery*, editor Michael DeBakey, 1957.

Faggella, M., Zuhdi, N., Greer, A., Carey, J., and Schilling, J.:
A method to eliminate air bubbles in a bubble type oxygenator. *American Journal of Surgery* 96: 696-697, 1958.

Zuhdi, N., Greer, A., Carey, J., Faggella, M., and Johnson, P.:
Experimental background for open-heart surgery at the University Hospital of Oklahoma City, Oklahoma. *Journal Oklahoma State Medical Association* 52: 15-17, 1959. (Projects state of the art of perfusion in 1958 when Zuhdi began his work in Oklahoma City)

Zuhdi, N., Joel, W., Greer, A., Carey, J., and Faggella, M.:
Cerebral changes during cardiopulmonary bypass using the helix reservoir bubble oxygenator. *The Journal of Thoracic and Cardiovascular Surgery* 37: 703-706, June 1959.

Zuhdi, N., Carey, J., and Greer, A.:
Aneurysms of the aorta. *Journal Oklahoma State Medical Association* 52: 587-592, 1959.

Zuhdi, N., Greer, A., Kimmell, G., Montroy, J., Redmond, R., McCollough, B., Carey, J., Geigerman, D., and Kreiger, C.:
A clinical study of hypothermic perfusion. *Journal Oklahoma State Medical Association* 52: 671-674, 1959.

Greer, A., Carey, J., and Zuhdi, N.:
Expeditious evaluation of circumscribed pulmonary shadows. *Journal American Medical Association* 171: 1783-1786, 1959.

Zuhdi, N., Kraft, D., Carey, J., and Greer, A.:
Coronary arteriovenous-like communication. *Archives of Surgery* 80: 178-180, 1960.

Zuhdi, N., McCollough, B., Carey, J., Montoroy, J., and Greer, A.:
Hypothermic total body cardiopulmonary bypass – report of nineteen consecutive cases. (includes addendum reporting total intentional hemodilution) *Journal Oklahoma State Medical Association* 53: 83-85, 1960.

Zuhdi, N., Kimmell, G., Carey, J., and Greer, A.:
Vacuum regulator for cardiotomy return and chest drainage systems. *Journal of Thoracic and Cardiovascular Surgery* 39: 221-224, 1960.

Zuhdi, N., Carey, J., and Greer, A.:
Research service development at Mercy Heart Center, Oklahoma City, Oklahoma. *Mercy Hospital Progress* 41: 74-76, 1960.

Carey, J., Zuhdi, N., and Greer, A.:
Thoracic surgery in the presence of pulmonary insufficiency and disability. *Disease of the Chest* 36: 576-578, 1960.

Zuhdi, N., Kimmell, G., Montroy, J., Carey, J., and Greer, A.:
A system for hypothermic perfusion. T*he Journal of Thoracic and Cardiovascular Surgery* 39: 629-633, 1960. (submitted 20 July 1959—shows status of perfusion before total intentional hemodilution)

Zuhdi, N., McCollough, B., Kimmell, G., Montroy, J., Carey, J., and Greer, A.:
Apparatus for hypothermic perfusion – clinical application. *American Surgeon* 26: 446-450, July 1960. (includes addendum by Zuhdi which reports total intentional hemodilution)

Zuhdi, N., McCollough, B., Carey, J., and Greer, A.:
Hypothermic total body cardiopulmonary bypass. Experimental and clinical studies. Journal Oklahoma State Medical Association 53: 514-516, 1960. (includes addendum by Zuhdi reporting total intentional hemodilution)

Zuhdi, N., McCollough, B., Carey, J., and Greer, A.:
The use of citrated bank blood for open-heart surgery. *Anesthesiology* 21:496-501, October 1960. (description of total intentional hemodilution)

Zuhdi, N., McCollough, B., Carey, J., Montroy, J., and Greer, A.:
Prolonged simple aortic occlusion during hypothermic perfusion as an aid to open-heart surgery – clinical application. *Postgraduate Medicine* 28: 507-509, 1960.

Greer, A., Carey, J., and Zuhdi, N.:
Hypothermic circulation with a temperature regulating pump oxygenator. *American Surgeon* 26: 770-772, 1960.

Zuhdi, N., McCollough, B., Carey, J., and Greer, A.:
Double helical reservoir heart-lung machine designed for hypothermic perfusion, primes with 5% dextrose in water, inducing hemodilution. *Archives of Surgery* 82: 320-325, 1961. (Synopsis – Abstract in Journal of the American Medical Association)

Zuhdi, N., McCollough, B., Carey, J., and Greer, A.:

Hypothermic perfusion for open-heart surgical procedures – report on the use of a heart-lung machine primed with 5% dextrose in water, inducing hemodilution. Journal of the International College of Surgeons 35: 319-326, 1961. *Condensed in the series of *Year Book of General Surgery,* editor Michael DeBakey, 220-221, 1962-1963.

Zuhdi, N.: Discussion of W.M. Chardack, et al., "Correction of complete heart block by a self-contained and subcutaneously implanted pacemaker." *The Journal of Thoracic and Cardiovascular Surgery* 42: 827-828, 1961.

Carey, J., Zuhdi, N., and Greer, A.:
Hypothermic perfusion – a clinical study in progress. *Journal of Arkansas Medical Society* 57: 453-456, 1961.

Carey, J., Zuhdi, N., Donnell, J., Honick, G., McCollum, W., Robbins, G., Kraft, D., Greer, A:
Open-heart surgery in a private hospital; clinical experience with 127 cases. *Journal Oklahoma State Medical Association* 54: 438-440, 1961.

Greer, A., Carey, J., and Zuhdi, N.:
A safe method for the open correction of mitral stenosis. *American Surgeon* 28: 266-269, 1962.

Zuhdi, N., Carey, J., and Greer, A.:
Transistor pacemaker for complete atrioventricular dissociation. *Journal Oklahoma State Medical Association* 55: 90, 1962.

Greer, A., Zuhdi, N., and Carey, J.:
Hemodilution principle of hypothermic perfusion: a concept obviating blood priming. *The Journal of Thoracic and Cardiovascular Surgery* 43: 640-648, 1962. *Condensed in the series of Cardiovascular and Renal Diseases, editors John W. Kirklin and others, 361-362, 1962-1963.

Zuhdi, N., Carey, J., and Greer, A.:
Hemodilution and coagulation factors in extracorporeal circulation. *The Journal of Thoracic and Cardiovascular Surgery* 43:816-821, 1962. *Condensed in the series of Year Book of Surgery, editor Michael DeBakey, 250-251, 1963-1964.

Zuhdi, N., Carey, J., and Greer, A.:
Hemodilution for body perfusion. *Journal Oklahoma State Medical Association* 56: 88-107, 1963.

Zuhdi, N., Guertzenstein, E., Carey, J., and Greer, A.:
Hemodilution circulacao extracorporeal. *Revista Brasileira de Cirurgia* 45: 318, 327, 1963.

Zuhdi, N., Carey, J., and Greer, A.:
Comparative merits and results of blood primes and 5% dextrose in water primes of heart-lung machines; analysis of 250 patients. *The Journal of Thoracic and Cardiovascular Surgery* 47: 66-78, January 1964. Presented at the American Association of Thoracic Surgeons, Houston, Texas, April 1963.

Zuhdi, N., Carey, J., Rader, L., Cutter, J., and Greer, A.:
Intentional hemodilution. *Archives of Surgery* 87: 554-559, October 1963.

Zuhdi, N., Carey, J., Sheldon, W., and Greer, A.:
Hemodilution, low flow rates and moderate internal hypothermia for extracorporeal circulation – concepts obviating the use of blood for priming. *Angiology* 14: 571-575, December 1963.

Zuhdi, N., Carey, J., Rader, L., and Greer, A.:
The techniques of hemodilution perfusion. *Journal of the International College of Surgeons* 41: 257-264, March 1964.

Zuhdi, N., Carey, J., and Greer, A.:
Blood, Mannitol, Dextran, sugar water and confusion. *The Bulletin of the South Central Association of Blood Banks* 7: 4-15, 1964.

Zuhdi, N., Carey, J., Schmidt, A., Mankin, H., and Greer, A.:
Total body perfusion and pregnancy. *Journal of the International College of Surgeons* 43: 43-46, 1965.

Zuhdi, N., Ritchie, C., Carey, J., and Greer, A.:
Assisted circulation – the concept of the implanted bypass heart – an experimental study. Annals of Thoracic Surgery 1: 229-243, 1965. *Condensed in the series of *Year Book of General Surgery*, editor Michael DeBakey, 58-61, 1966-1967.

Zuhdi, N., Carey, J., Pierce, M., Rickey, O., Greer, A.:
Present status of simplified body perfusion. *Journal Oklahoma State Medical Association* 58: 112-117, 1965.

Zuhdi, N., Bynum, E., Carey, J., and Greer, A.:
Intramedullary fixation of sternum in fractures of sternum and corrective procedures for funnel chest. *The Journal of Thoracic and Cardiovascular Surgery* 50: 83-85, 1965.

Carey, J., Greer, A., Honick, G., Bressie, J., and Zuhdi, N.:
Myxoma of the left artrium. *Annals of Thoracic Surgery* 1: 736-741, 1965.

Zuhdi, N., Carey, J., and Greer, A:
The permanently implanted bypass heart. *The Journal of Thoracic and Cardiovascular Surgery* 50: 800-810, 1965.

Greer, A., Carey, J., and Zuhdi, N.:
Evaluation of preoperative radiation of bronchogenic carcinoma. *American Journal of Surgery* 110: 732-736, 1965.

Zuhdi, N., Carey, J., Musa, N., Rickey, O., and Greer, A.:
Total replacement of aortic valve. *Journal Oklahoma State Medical Association* 58: 540-543, 1965.

Zuhdi, N., Carey, J., Newton, M., and Greer, A.:
Evaluation of a technique to prevent aortic regurgitation using the Magovern prosthesis. *Annals of Thoracic Surgery* 2: 617-620, 1966.

Zuhdi, N., Waldrop, W., Carey, J., and Greer, A.:
Intramedullary fixation of sternum. *Journal Oklahoma State Medical Association* 59: 677, 1966.

Zuhdi, N., Musa, M., Carey, J., and Greer, A.:
A wrapping technique for the Magovern aortic prosthesis. *Annals of Thoracic Surgery* 2: 4, 617-620, July 1966.

Zuhdi, N.: Discussion of L. Gonzalez-Lavin and T. O'Connell; Mitral valve replacement with viable aortic homograft valves. *Annals of Thoracic Surgery* 15: 592-600, 1973.

Zuhdi, N., Hancock, W., Hawley, W., Carey, J., and Greer, A:
Porcine aortic valves for replacement of human heart valves. The Journal of Thoracic and Cardiovascular Surgery, Special Issue: 425-429, 1973. *Condensed in the *Year Book of Cardiovascular Medicine,* editors John W. Kirklin and others, 391, 1975.

Zuhdi, N.: Discussion of R.B. Wallace, S.P. Londe, and J.L. Titus: Aortic valve replacement with preserved aortic valve homografts. *The Journal of Thoracic and Cardiovascular Surgery* 67: 51-52, 1974.

Zuhdi, N., Hawley, W., Voehl, V., Hancock, W., Carey, J., and Greer, A.:
Porcine aortic valves as replacements for human heart valves. *Annals of Thoracic Surgery* 72: 479-491, 1974.

Zuhdi, N.: Discussion of E. Stinson, R. Griepp, and N. Shumway:
Porcine aortic valve xenograft for mitral valve replacement. *Annals of Thoracic Surgery* 18: 399-400, 1974.

Zuhdi, N.: Discussion of A. Carpentier et al.:
Six-year follow up of glutaraldehyde preserved heterografts. *The Journal of Thoracic and Cardiovascular Surgery* 68: 781-782, 1974.

Zuhdi, N.:
The porcine aortic valve bioprosthesis: a significant alternative. *Annals of Thoracic Surgery* 21: 573-575, 1976.

Zuhdi, N: Discussion: valve substitutes.
2nd Henry Ford Hospital International Symposium on Cardiac Surgery, (Julia Davila, Editor), p. 441, 1977.

Zuhdi, N.: Discussion:
Porcine valves. *Annals of Thoracic Surgery* 37: 78-83, 1984.

Novitzky, D., Cooper, D.K.C., and Zuhdi, N.:
The physiological management of cardiac transplant donors and recipients using Triiodothyronine. *Transplantation Proceeding* 20: 803-805, 1988.

Cooper, D.K.C., Sumpter, P., Novitzky, D., Chaffin, J.S., Greer, A., Barnard, C.N., and Zuhdi, N.:
Assessment and selection of patients for heart transplantation at Baptist Medical Center. *Journal Oklahoma State Medical Association* 41: 137-140, 1988.

Cooper, D.K.C., Romero, C.A., Clark, R.M., Chaffin, J.S., Greer, A., Novitzky, D., Barnard, C.N., and Zuhdi, N.:
Indications for heterotopic heart transplantation and report of two patients. *Journal Oklahoma State Medical Association* 81: 513-517, 1988.

Novitzky, D., Cooper, D.K.C., and Zuhdi, N.:
Triiodothyronine therapy in the cardiac transplant recipient. *Transplantation Proceeding* 20: 5, 65-68, October 1988.

Novitzky, D., Cooper, D.K.C., Human, P.A., Reichart, B., and Zuhdi, N.:
Triiodothyronine therapy for heart donor and recipient. *Journal of Heart Transplantation* 7: 370-376, 1988.

Novitzky, D., Cooper, D.K.C., Barton, C., Greer, A., Chaffin, J.S., Grim, J., and Zuhdi, N.:
Triiodothyronine (T3) as an inotropic agent after open-heart surgery. *The Journal of Thoracic and Cardiovascular Surgery* 98: 972-978, 1989.

Novitzky, D., Cooper, D.K.C., Muchmore, J.S., and Zuhdi, N.:
Pituitary function in brain-dead patients (letter). *Transplantation* 48: 1078-1079, 1989.

Zuhdi, N., Novitzky, D., Shrago, S.S., Clark, R.M., Voda, J., Cooper, D.K.C.:
Experience with endomyocardial biopsy in 23 patients with heart transplants. *Journal Oklahoma State Medical Association* 82: 109-111, 1989.

Cooper, D.K.C., Novitzky, D., Davis, L., Huff, J.E., Parker, D., Schlesinger, R., Sholer, C., and Zuhdi, N.:
Does central nervous system toxicity occur in transplant patients with hypocholesterolemia receiving cyclosporine? *Journal of Heart Transplantation* 8: 221-224, 1989.

Tamez, A., Cooper, D.K.C., Novitzky, D., Chaffin, J.S., Greer, A., and Zuhdi, N.:
Experience with cardiorespiratory support devices in patients undergoing heart and heart-lung transplantation. *Journal Oklahoma State Medical Association* 83: 449-453, September 1990.

Novitzky, D., Cooper, D.K.C., Chaffin, J.S., Greer, A., DeBault, L.E., and Zuhdi, N.:
Improved cardiac allograft function following triiodothyronine therapy to both donor and recipient. *Transplantation* 49: 2, 311-316, 1990.

Muchmore, J.S., Cooper, D.K.C., Ye, Y., Schlegal, V., and Zuhdi, N.:
Loss of vertebral bone density in heart transplant patients. *Transplantation Proceeding* 23: 1184-1185, 1991.

Novitzky, D., Matthews, N., Shawley, D., Cooper, D.K.C., and Zuhdi, N.:
Triiodothyronine in the recovery of stunned myocardium in dogs. *Annals of Thoracic Surgery* 51: 10-17, 1991.

Mues, B., Brisse, B., Steinhoff, G., Lynn, T., Hewett, T., Sorg, C., and Zuhdi, N.:
Diagnostic assessment of macrophage phenotypes in cardiac transplant biopsies. *European Heart Journal*, 1991.

Cooper, D.K.C., Novitzky, D., Schlegal, V., Muchmore, J.S., Cucchiarra, A., and Zuhdi, N.:
Successful management of symptomatic cytomegalovirus disease by ganciclovir following heart transplantation. *Journal of Heart Transplantation* (Abstract 9: 59, 1990) 10: 656-663, 1991.

Welch, R.W., Yokoyama, Y., Cooper, D.K.C., and Zuhdi, N.:
The gastrointestinal management of patients undergoing heart transplantation. *Journal Oklahoma State Medical Association* 84: 557-562, 1991.

Sundararajan, V., Cooper, D.K.C., Muchmore, J.S., Manion, C.V., Luguori, C., and Zuhdi, N.:
Interaction of cyclosporine and probucol in heart transplanted patients. *Transplantation Proceeding* 23 (3): 2028-2032, 1991.

Yokoyama, Y., Cooper, D.K.C., and Zuhdi, N.:
Risk of endocarditis in donor hearts (letter). *Journal of Heart & Lung Transplantation* 10: 618, 1991.

Jazzar, A.S., Dalton, W.E., Bradley, N.E., Cooper, D.K.C., and Zuhdi, N.:
A methyl methacrylate plate to prevent compression following heart transplantation. *Annals of Thoracic Surgery* 55: 1243-1244, 1993.

Jazzar, A.S., Cooper, D.K.C., Muchmore, J.S., Pribil, A., Chaffin, J.S., and Zuhdi, N.:
Heart transplantation with low mortality and low morbidity. *Saudi Heart Journal* 3: 33-41, 1992.

Cooper, D.K.C, and Zuhdi, N.:
Current patient survival following heart or single lung transplantation at Baptist Medical Center. Bulletin, Oklahoma County Medical Society 23: 25-26, March 1992.

Chaffin, J.S., Cooper, D.K.C., and Zuhdi, N.:
Donor organ availability. *Journal Oklahoma State Medical Association* 85: 111-114, 1992.

Cooper, D.K.C., Muchmore, J.S., and Zuhdi, N.:
The assessment of the results of heart transplantation. *Journal of Heart &*

*Lung Transplantation* 11: 165-166, 1992.

Nickrasz, M., Ye, Y., Rolf, L.L., Zuhdi, N., and Cooper, D.K.C.:
The pig as organ donor for man. *Transplantation Proceeding* 24: 625-626, 1992.

Baker, J., Martin, M., Ye, Y., Oleinick, S., and Zuhdi, N.:
Presence of a complement-dependent "cytotoxic factor" in dog serum: relevance to experimental discordant xenotransplantation. *Transplantation Proceeding* 24: 490-491, 1992.

Cooper, D.K.C., Ye, Y., Kehoe, M., Niekrasz, M., Rolf, L.L., Martin, M., Baker, J., Kosanke, S., Zuhdi, N., Worsley, G., and Romano, E.:
A novel approach to "neutralization" of preformed antibodies: cardiac allotransplantation across the ABO-blood group barrier as a paradigm of discordant xenotransplantation. *Transplantation Proceeding* 24: 566-571, 1992.

Debault, L., Ye, Y., Rolf, L.L., Niekrasz, M., Kosanke, S., Zuhdi, N., and Cooper, D.K.C.:
Ultrastructural features in hyperacutely rejected baboon cardiac allografts and pig cardiac xenografts. *Transplantation Proceeding* 24: 612-613, 1992.

Good, H., Cooper, D.K.C., Malcolm, A.J., Ippolito, R.M., Koren, E., Neethling, F.A., Ye, Y., and Zuhdi, N.:
Identification of carbohydrate structures with bind human anti-porcine antibodies: implications for discordant xenografting in man. *Transplantation Proceeding* 24: 559-562, 1992.

Koren, E., Neethling, F.A., Ye, Y., Niekrasz, M., Baker, J., Martin, M., Zuhdi, N., and Cooper, D.K.C.:
Heterogeneity of preformed human anti-pig xenogeneic antibodies. *Transplantation Proceeding* 24: 598-601, 1992.

Niekrasz, M., Ye, Y., Rolf, L.L., Zuhdi, N., Cooper, D.K.C.:
The pig as organ donor for man. *Transplantation Proceeding* 24: 625-626, 1992.

Ye, Y., Cooper, D.K.C., Niekrasz, M., Rolf, L.L., Koren, E., Baker, J., Martin, M., Smith, J., and Zuhdi, N.:
Removal of dog anti-pig antibody by absorption with pig red blood cell stroma columns. *Transplantation Proceeding* 24: 563-565, 1992.

Yokoyama, Y., Cooper, D.K.C., Sasaki, H., Akutsu, T., and Zuhdi, N.:
Donor heart evaluation by monitoring the left ventricular pressure-volume relationship: Clinical Observations. *Journal of Heart & Lung Transplantation* 11: 685-692, 1992.

Muchmore, J.S., Cooper, D.K.C., Ye, Y., Schlegal, V., and Zuhdi, N.:
Prevention of loss of vertebral bone density in heart transplant patients. *Journal of Heart & Lung Transplantation* 11: 959-964, 1992.

Jazzar, A., Cooper, D.K.C., and Zuhdi, N.:
Cytomegalovirus disease in heart transplant patients. *Transplantation* 53: 5, 1167-1168, 1992.

Cooper, D.K.C., and Zuhdi, N.:
Angina pectoris in patients with cardiac transplants. *Clinical Transplantation* 6: 2, 139-140, April 1992.

Jazzar, A., Dalton, W.E., Bradley, N., Koren, E., Cooper, D.K.C., and Zuhdi, N.:
Methyl methacrylate plate to prevent compression after heart transplantation. *Annals of Thoracic Surgery* 55: 1242-1243, 1993.

Jazzar, A., Cooper, D.K.C., Muchmore, J.S., Pribil, A., Chaffin, J.S., and Zuhdi, N.:
A successful regimen to reduce cytomegalovirus disease in heart transplant patients. *Transplantation* 4: 47-53, 1993.

Cooper, D.K.C., Good, H., Ye, Y., Koren, E., Oriol, R., Ippolito, R.M., Malcolm, A.J., Neethling, F.A., Romano, E., and Zuhdi, N.:
Specific intravenous carbohydrate therapy: A new approach to the inhibition of antibody-mediated rejection following ABO-incompatible allografting and discordant xenografting. *Transplantation Proceeding* 25: 377-378, 1993.

Imes, N., Cooper, D.K.C., and Zuhdi, N.:
Initial experience with single lung transplantation in Oklahoma. *Journal Oklahoma State Medical Association* 86: 16-22, 1993.

Cooper, D.K.C., Ye, Y., Niekrasz, M., Kehoe, M., Martin, M., Neethling, F.A., Kosanke, S., DeBault, L.E., Worsley, G., Zuhdi, N., Oriol, R., and Romano, E.:
Specific intravenous carbohydrate therapy: A new concept in inhibiting antibody-mediated rejection – experience with ABO – Incompatible cardiac allografting in the baboon. *Transplantation* 56: 5, 769-777, 1993.

Cooper, D.K.C., Ye, Y., Chaffin, J.S., Zuhdi, N.:
A suggested technique for "orthotopic" heart transplantation in a patient with situs inversus. *Texas Heart Institute Journal* 20: 281-284, 1993.

Cooper, D.K.C., Good, A.H., Koren, E., Oriol, R., Malcolm, A.J., Illpolito, R.M., Neethling, F.A., Ye, Y., Romano, E., and Zuhdi, N.:
Identification of a-galactosyl and other carbohydrate epitopes that are bound by human anti-pig antibodies: relevance to discordant xenografting in man. *Transplant Immunology* 1: 198-205, 1993.

Koren E., Neethling, F.A., Richards, S.V., Koscec, M., Ye, Y., Zuhdi, N., and Cooper, D.K.C.:
Binding and specificity of major immunoglobulin classes of preformed human anti-pig heart antibodies. *Transplant International* 6: 351-353, 1993.

Cooper, D.K.C., Schlesinger, R.G., Shrago, S., and Zuhdi, N.:
Letter to the Editor: Heart transplantation for giant cell myocarditis. *Journal of Heart & Lung Transplantation* 13: 4. 1994.

Paris, W., Muchmore, J., Pribil, A., Zuhdi, N., and Cooper, D.K.C.:
Study of the relative incidences of psychosocial factors before and after heart transplantation and the influence of post-transplantation psychosocial factors on heart transplantation outcome. *Journal of Heart & Lung Transplantation* 13: 3, 1994.

Ye, Y., Niekrasz, M., Kehoe, M., Rolf, L., Martin, M., Baker, J., Kosanke, S., Romano, E., Zuhdi, N., and Cooper, D.K.C.:
Cardiac allotransplantation across the ABO-blood group barrier by the neutralization of preformed antibodies: the baboon as a model for the human. *Laboratory of Animal Science* 44: 2, 1994.

Koren, E., Kujundzic, M., Koscec, M., Neethling, F.A., Richards, S.V., Ye, Y., Zuhdi, N., and Cooper, D.K.C.:
Cytotoxic effects of human performed anti-gal IgG and complement on cultured pig cells. *Transplantation Proceeding* 26: 1336-1339, 1994.

Ye, Y., Niekrasz, M., Welch, R., Maxwell, C., Zuhdi, N., and Cooper, D.K.C.:
A practical study of zoonoses that could complicate pig-to-man organ transplantation. *Transplantation Proceeding* 26: 1312, 1994.

Cooper, D.K.C., Samara, E.N.S., Mieles, L., Merhav, H., Imes, N., VanThiel, D.H., and Zuhdi, N.:
Survival following organ transplantation in an Oklahoma Institution, 1985-1993. *Journal Oklahoma State Medical Association* 87: 506-508, 1994.

Jazzar, A., Fagiuoli, S., Caraceni, P., Deal, S., Wright, H.I., Sisson, S., Gavaler, J., VanThiel, D.H., Zuhdi, N., and Cooper, D.K.C.:
Incidence and etiology of hepatic dysfunction in heart transplant recipients receiving a cyclosporine-based triple immune-suppressive therapy. *Transplantation Proceeding* 26: 2654, 1994.

Jazzar, A., Fagiuoli, S., Sisson, S., Zuhdi, N., and Cooper, D.K.C.:
Induction therapy with cyclosporine and without cytolytic agent results in a low incidence of acute rejection without significant renal impairment in heart transplant patients. *Transplantation Proceeding* 26: 2749, 1994; *Clinical Transplantation* 9: 334-339, 1995.

Sisson, S., Tripp, J., Paris, W., Cooper, D.K.C., and Zuhdi, N.:
Medication non-compliance and its relationship to financial factors after heart transplantation (Letter). *Journal of Heart & Lung Transplantation* 13: 930, 1994.

VanThiel, D.H., Baddour, H., Gavaler, J.S., Fagiuoli, S., Caraceni, P., Wright, H.I., and Zuhdi, N.:
Acute and chronic sinusitis: A cause of unsuspected pathology in patients with end-stage liver disesase. *European Journal of Gastroenterology and Hepatology* 6: 1153-1155, 1994.

Ye, Y., Niekrasz, M., Welsh, R., Jordan, H., Maxwell, C., Zuhdi, N., and Cooper, D.K.C.:
The pig as potential organ donor for man. A study of potentially tranferable disease from donor pig to recipient man. *Transplantation* 57: 694-703, 1994. *Presented to the International Society for Heart and Lung Transplantation, Boca Raton, 1993.

VanThiel, D.H., Fagiuoli, S., Caraceni, P., Wright, H.I., Nadir, A., Gavaler, J.S., and Zuhdi, N.:
Cryoglobulinemia: A cause for false negative polymerase chain reaction results in patients with hepatitis C virus positive chronic liver disease. *Journal of Hepatology* 22: 464-467, 1995.

Nadir, A., Wright, H.I., Naz-Nadir, F., Cooper, D.K.C., Zuhdi, N., and VanThiel, D.H.:
Atypical Clostridium difficile colitis in a heart transplant recipient (Letter). *Journal of Heart & Lung Transplantation* 14: 606-607, 1995.

Jazzar, A., Fagiuoli, S., Sisson, S., Zuhdi, N., and Cooper, D.K.C.:
Induction therapy with cyclosporine without cytolytic agents results in a low incidence of acute rejection without significant renal impairment in heart transplant patients. *Clinical Transplantation* 9: 334-339, 1995.

VanThiel, D.H., Molloy, P.J., Friedlander, L., Kania, R.J., Fagiuoli, S., Caraceni, P., Wright, H.I., and Zuhdi, N.:
Interferon a treatment of chronic hepatitis C in patients with evidence for co-existent autoimmune dysregulation. *Hepatogastroenterology* 42: 900-906, 1995.

Paris, W., Cooper, D.K.C., Samara, S., Carpenter, W., Crockett, S., Calhoun-Wilson, G., Quinsenberry, M., and Zuhdi, N.:
A comparison of organ transplant patient and professional staff attitudes. *International Journal of Rehabilitation and Health* 1: 3, 1995.

Mischke, L., Sisson, S., Cooper, D.K.C., and Zuhdi, N.:

Cardiac transplantation in patients aged 60 years or older. *Journal Oklahoma State Medical Association* 89: 22-25, 1996.

Zuhdi, N.:
Zuhdi relates history of his modified DeWall-Lillehei heart-lung machine. *Journal Oklahoma State Medical Association* 89: 300-301, 1996.

Sisson, S., Jazzar, A., Mischke, L., Cooper, D.K.C., and Zuhdi, N.:
How many endomyocardial biopsies (EMB's) are necessary in the first year after heart transplantation? *Transplant International* 9: 243-247, 1996.

Taniguchi, S., Chaffin, J.S., Cooper, D.K.C., and Zuhdi, N.:
Primary bronchogenic carcinoma in recipients of heart transplants. *Transplantation International* 10: 312-316, 1997.

Paradis, I.L., and Zuhdi, N.:
Lung transplantation in 1997. *Revista Chilena de Enfermedades Respiratorias* 13: 146-164, 1997.

Fagiuoli, S., Cooper, D.K.C., and Zuhdi, N.:
Hepatitis C status of heart transplant recipient. *Clinical Transplantation* 12: 5-10, 1998.

## CHAPTERS IN BOOKS

1967  *Cardiac Surgery*
Nazih Zuhdi, M.D.: Hypothermic and Hemodilution Techniques, Chapter 8, pp. 99-130. John C. Norman, Editor, Appleton Century-Crofts, Publishers.

1972  *Cardiac Surgery*
Nazih Zuhdi, M.D.: Hypothermic and Hemodilution Techniques, Chapter 8, pp. 159-182. John C. Norman, Editor, Appleton Century-Crofts, Publishers.

1990  *Transplanting the Human Heart*
Nazih Zuhdi, M.D.: Results of Organ Transplantation, pp. 81-82. David K.C. Cooper, William F. Carpenter, Margaret Ball, and Nazih Zuhdi, Editors.

1990  *Xenotransplantation*
D.K.C. Cooper, Y. Ye, L.L. Rolf, Jr., and Nazih Zuhdi: The Pig as Potential Organ Donor for Man, Chapter 30, pp. 481-500. David K.C. Cooper, E. Kemp, K. Reemtsma, D.J.G. White, Editors.

1992  *Chris Barnard, By Those Who Know Him*
Nazih Zuhdi, M.D.: The Inner Man, pp. 357-361. David K.C. Cooper, Editor.

## FOREWORD

1990  *The Transplantation and Replacement of Thoracic Organs*, editors David K.C. Cooper and Dimitri Novitzky. Forward by Christiaan Barnard and Nazih Zuhdi.

## PAPERS PRESENTED AT MAJOR MEETINGS AS PRESENTER AND/OR CO-AUTHOR

Acid-base balance during prolonged cardiopulmonary bypass. Paneth, M., Zuhdi, N., and Weirich, W. Presented to the American Association for Thoracic Surgery, Chicago, 1957.

Hypothermic total body cardiopulmonary bypass, experimental and clinical studies. Zuhdi, N., McCollough, B., Carey, J., and Greer, A. Presented to the Oklahoma County Heart Association, Oklahoma City, 1960.

Comparative merits and results of primes of blood and 5% dextrose in water for heart-lung machines; analysis of 250 patients. Zuhdi, N., Carey, J., and Greer, A. Presented to the American Association for Thoracic Surgery, Houston, 1963.

Hemodilution for extracorporeal circulation – concepts obviating the use of blood for priming. Zuhdi, N., Carey, J., Sheldon, W., and Greer, A. Presented to the International College of Angiology, San Jaun, Puerto Rico, 1963.

The concept of the permanently implanted bypass heart – an experimental study. Zuhdi, N., Carey, J., and Greer, A. Presented to the Honduras Chapter of the American College of Chest Physicians, Tegucicalpa, Honduras, 1964.

Myxoma of the left atrium. Carey, J., Greer, A., Honick, G., Bressie, J., and Zuhdi, N. Presented to the Society of Thoracic Surgeons, 1965.

The permanently implanted bypass heart. Zuhdi, N., Carey, J., and Greer, A. Presented to the American Association for Thoracic Surgery, 1965.

Evaluation of preoperative radiation of bronchogenic carcinoma. Greer, A., Carey, J., and Zuhdi, N. Presented to the Southwestern Surgical Congress, Hot Springs, 1965.

Evaluation of a technique to prevent aortic regurgitation using the Magovern prosthesis. Zuhdi, N., Carey, J., Newton, M., and Greer, A. Presented to the Society of Thoracic Surgeons, Denver, 1966.

A Wrapping technique for Magovern aortic prosthesis. Zuhdi, N., Musa, N., Carey, J., and Greer, A. Presented to the Second Annual Meeting of the Society of Thoracic Surgeons, Denver, 1966.

Porcine aortic valve for replacement of human heart valves. Zuhdi, N., Hancock, W., Hawley, W., Carey, J., and Greer, A. Presented to the Eleventh World Congress of the International Cardiovascular Society, Barcelona, Spain, 1973.

Triiodothyronine (T3) as an inotropic agent following open-heart surgery. Novitzky, D., Cooper, D.K.C., Barton, C., Greer, A., Chaffin, J.S., and Zuhdi, N. Presented to the C.Walton Lillehei Surgical Symposium, Minneapolis, 1988.

Triiodothyronine therapy for heart donor and recipient. Novitzky, D., Cooper, D.K.C., Reichart, B., and Zuhdi, N. Presented to Eighth Scientific Sessions of the International Society for Heart Transplantation, Los Angeles, 1988.

Improved cardiac allograft function following triiodothyronine (T3) therapy to both donor and recipient. Novitzky, D., Cooper, D.K.C., Chaffin, J.S., Greer, A., DeBault, L.E., and Zuhdi, N. Presented to the American Society of Transplant Surgeons, Chicago, 1989.

Triiodothyronine (T3) in the recovery of stunned myocardium in dogs. Novitzky, D., Matthews, N., Shawley, R., Cooper, D.K.C., and Zuhdi, N. Presented to the Society of Thoracic Surgeons, Baltimore, 1989.

Interference with steady state cyclosporine levels by probucol. Corder, C.N., Sundararajan, V., Liguori, C., Cooper, D.K.C., Muchmore, J.,

and Zuhdi, N. Presented to the X International Symposium On Drugs Affecting Lipid Metabolism, Houston, 1989.

Waiting for a Heart – The Oklahoma Experience. Jackson, W.E., Cooper, D.K.C., Novitzky, D., and Zuhdi, N. Presented to the Oklahoma Transplantation Society, Tulsa, 1989.

Clinical survey of heart transplantation between ABO-blood group incompatible recipients and donor. Presented as a poster to the Ninth Annual Scientific Sessions of the International Society for Heart Transplantation, Munich, 1989.

Acute inotropic response of rabbit papillary muscle to triiodothyronine (T3). Snow, T.R., Novitzky, D., Deal, M., and Zuhdi, N. Presented to the Federated American Society of Experimental Biology, Washington, D.C., 1990.

Successful management of cytomegalovirus disease by ganciclovir following heart transplantation, and relationship with early incidence of accelerated graft atherosclerosis. Cooper, D.K.C., Novitzky, D., Schlegal, V., and Zuhdi, N. Presented to the International Society for Heart Transplantation, Ft. Lauderdale, 1990.

Immunosuppression in cardiac transplantation and expression of a specific microphage phenotype within the myocardium. Mues, B., Robbins, G., Brisse, B., Steinhoff, G., Sorg, C., Lynn, T., and Zuhdi, N. Presented to the American Society of Transplant Surgeons, Chicago, 1990.

The left ventricular ejection fraction as determined by technetium-99m (Tc-99m) is a reliable indicator that graft atherosclerosis is developing. Novitzky, D., Cooper, D.K.C., Boniaszczuk, J., Harolds, J., and Zuhdi, N. Presented to American Society of Transplant Surgeons, Chicago, 1990.

Assessment of macrophage phenotypes in cardiac transplant biopsies. Mues, B., Robbins, G., Brisse, B., Steinhoff, G., Sorg, C., Lynn, T., and Zuhdi, N. Presented to the Second International Symposium On Inflammatory Heart Disease, Marburg, Germany, 1990.

Donor heart evaluation by monitoring the left ventricular pressure-volume relationship: experimental and clinical observations. Yokoyama, Y., Cooper, D.K.C., Sasaki, H., Akutsu, T., and Zuhdi, N. Presented as a poster to International Society for Heart and Lung Transplantation, Paris, 1991.

Prevention of loss of vertebral bone density in heart transplant patients. Muchmore, J.S., Cooper, D.K.C., Ye, Y., Schlegal, V., and Zuhdi, N. Presented to the International Society for Heart Transplantation, Paris, 1991 and as a poster to the American Society of Transplant Physicians, Chicago, 1991.

Presence of a complement-dependent "cytotoxic factor" in dog serum: relevance to experimental discordant xenotransplantation. Baker, J., Martin, M., Ye, Y., Olenick, S., Zuhdi, N., and Cooper, D.K.C. Presented to the First International Congress on Xenotransplantation, Minneapolis, 1991.

A novel approach to "neutralization" of preformed antibodies; cardiac allotransplantation across the ABO-blood group barrier as a paradigm of discordant xenotransplantation. Cooper, D.K.C., Ye, Y., Kehoe, M., Niekrasz, M., Rolf, L.L. Jr., Martin, M., Baker, J., Kosanke, S., Zuhdi, N., Worsley, G., and Romano, E. Presented to the First International Congress on Xenotransplantation, Minneapolis, 1991.

Ultrastructural features in hyperacutely rejected baboon cardiac allografts and pig cardiac xenografts. DeBault, L., Ye, Y., Rolf, L.L., Niekrasz, M., Kosanke, S., Zuhdi, N., and Cooper, D.K.C. Presented as a poster to the First International Congress on Xenotransplantation, Minneapolis, 1991.

Identification of carbohydrate structures which bind human anti-porcine antibodies: implications for discordant xenografting in man. Good, H., Cooper, D.K.C., Malcolm, A.J., Ippolito, R.M., Koren, E., Neethling, F.A., Ye, Y., and Zuhdi, N. Presented to the First International Congress on Xenotransplantation, Minneapolis, 1991.

Heterogeneity of preformed human anti-pig xenogeneic antibodies. Koren, E., Neethling, F.A., Ye, Y., Niekrasz, M., Baker, J., Martin, M., Zuhdi, N., and Cooper, D.K.C. Presented to the First International Congress on Xenotransplantation, Minneapolis, 1991.

The pig as organ donor for man. Niekrasz, M., Ye, Y., Rolf, L.L., Zuhdi, N., and Cooper, D.K.C. Presented as a poster to the First International Congress on Xenotransplantation, Minneapolis, 1991.

Removal of dog anti-pig antibody by adsorption with pig red blood cell stroma columns. Ye, Y., Cooper, D.K.C., Niekrasz, M., Rolf, L.L. Jr., Koren, E., Baker, J., Martin, M., Smith, J., and Zuhdi, N. Presented to the First International Congress on Xenotransplantation, Minneapolis, 1991.

Ultrastructural features in hyperacutely rejected baboon cardiac allografts and pig cardiac xenografts. DeBault, L., Ye, Y., Rolf, L.L., Niekrasz, M., Kasanke, S., and Zuhdi, N. Presented as a poster to the First International Congress on Xenotransplantation, Minneapolis, 1991.

Cardiac allotransplantation across the ABO-blood group barrier in the baboon by the "neutralization" of preformed antibodies: significance for discordant transplantation. Ye, Y., Kehoe, M., Niekrasz, M., Rolf, L.L., Martin, M., Baker, J., Kosanke, S., Romano, E., Zuhdi, N., and Cooper, D.K.C. Presented to the International Society for Heart and Lung Transplantation, San Diego, 1992.

Major immunoglobulin classes of preformed human anti-pig antibodies. Koren, E., Neethling, F. A., Ye, Y., Zuhdi, N., and Cooper, D.K.C. Presented to the International Society for Heart and Lung Transplantation, San Diego, 1992.

A successful regimen to reduce cytomegalovirus disease in heart transplant patients. Jazzar, A., Cooper, D.K.C., Muchmore, J.S., Pribil, A., Chaffin, J.S., and Zuhdi, N. Presented to the American Society of Transplant Surgeons, Chicago, 1992.

Heart Transplantation with low mortality and low morbidity. Cooper, D.K.C., and Zuhdi, N. Presented to the 25th Anniversary of the First Heart Transplant, Cape Town, 1992.

Specific intravenous carbohydrate therapy – a new approach to the inhibition of antibody-mediated rejection following ABO-incompatible allografting and discordant xenografting. Cooper, D.K.C., Ye, Y., Neethling, F.A., Koren, E., and Zuhdi, N. Presented to the 25th Anniversary of the First Heart Transplant, Cape Town, 1992.

Binding and specificity of major immunoglobulin classes of preformed human anti-pig heart antibodies. Koren, E., Neethling, F.A., Richards, S.V., Koscec, M., Ye, Y., Zuhdi, N., and Cooper, D.K.C. Presented to the International Society for Heart and Lung Transplantation, San Diego, 1992.

A practical study of zoonoses that could complicate pig-to-man organ transplantation. Ye, Y., Niekrasz, M., Welch, R., Kosanke, S., Maxwell, C., Zuhdi, N., and Cooper, D.K.C. Presented to the Second International Congress on Xenotransplantation, Cambridge, 1993.

Specific carbohydrates protect pig cells from the cytotoxic effects of human and baboon sera. Neethling, F.A., Koren, E., Richards, S.V., Ye, Y., Oriol, R., Zuhdi, N., and Cooper, D.K.C. Presented to the International Society for Heart and Lung Transplantation, Boca Raton, 1993.

Heart transplantation donor/recipient selection, management and complications. Jazzar, A., Cooper, D.K.C., Ye, Y., Chaffin, J., and Zuhdi, N. Annual Scientific Session of the American College for Internal Medicine, Washington, 1993.

The pig as potential organ donor for man. A study of potentially transferable disease from donor pig to recipient man. Ye, Y., Niekrasz, M., Welsh, R., Jordan, H., Maxwell, C., Zuhdi, N., and Cooper, D.K.C. Presented to the International Society for Heart and Lung Transplantation, Boca Raton, 1993.

Study of the relative incidences of psychosocial factors before and after heart transplantation and influences of post transplantation psychosocial factors on heart transplantation outcome. Paris, W., Muchmore, J., Pribil, A., Zuhdi, N., and Cooper, D.K.C. Presented at the Thirteenth Annual Meeting and Scientific Session of the International Society for Heart and Lung Transplantation, Boca Raton, 1993.

How many endomyocardial biopsies (EMB's) are necessary in the first year after heart transplantation? Sisson, S., Jazzar, A., Mischke, L., Cooper, D.K.C., and Zuhdi, N. Presented to the International Society for Heart and Lung Transplantation, San Francisco, 1995.

Prevalence of HCV infection after heart transplant. Fagiuoli, S., Jazzar, A., Demaria, N., Faruki, H., Deal, S., Hassanein, T., Colantoni, A., Sisson, S., Tripp, J., Gavaler, J.S., VanThiel, D.H., Cooper, D.K.C, and Zuhdi, N. (Missing the presented at part)

Digestive Disease Week of the American Gastroenterological Society and the American Association for the Study of Liver Diseases, San Diego, 1995; Italian Society for the Study of the Liver, Rome, 1995; Seventh Congress of the European Society for Organ Transplantation, Vienna, 1995; European Society for the Study of the Liver, Copenhagen, 1995.

**EDITORSHIP**

Guest editors, David K.C. Cooper, Dimitri Novitzky, and Nazih Zuhdi: Transplantation Proceedings: "Hormonal Therapy – A New Concept in the Management of Organ Donors," Vol. XX, No. 5, Suppl 7, October 1988.

Editors David K.C. Cooper, William F. Carpenter, Margaret A. Ball, and Nazih Zuhdi: "Transplanting the Human Heart," Vol. I, 1990.

*The Life of Nazih Zuhdi:*
*Uncharted Voyage of a Heart*